D1106360

ADAMSON

THE HILLS OF THE BOASTING WOMAN

The Hills of the
Boasting Woman

STEPHEN EARL

Readers Union · Peter Davies
LONDON 1963

To

RAFAEL RESTREPO

and

SÍMON SANCHEZ-GUTIERREZ

This RU edition was produced in 1963 for sale to its members only by Readers Union Ltd at Aldine House, 10-13 Bedford Street, London W.C.2 and at Letchworth Garden City, Herts. Full details of membership may be obtained from our London address. The book is set in 11 point Baskerville type leaded and has been printed at the Hollen Street Press, London W.1. It was first published by Peter Davies Ltd.

Preface

BETWEEN the Eastern range of the Andes in Colombia and the river Orinoco lie five hundred miles of grass, flat as the sea. Heavy forests stand in the richest or wettest places.

There were no grazing animals and the land was nearly empty when the Spanish came. They established cattle ranches, many administered by the Jesuits. In 1815 the plainsmen rose under Paez and Bolívar, and fought from Caracas in Venezuela to Peru. They never gave in. Many did not return, and the cattle were gone.

There have been troubles since, and few people are living in the plain. It is difficult, partly because disease and pests coming from the woods flourish on the cattle. Vampire bats and jaguars are not the worst.

It seemed there would be useful work for a zoologist, and the generosity of the Colombian government enabled me to go for a short time. I spent nearly all the season hunting in the woods; and it became an end in itself.

This account may be misleading in parts, and the names used for the animals are not precise. More accurate names and theoretical arguments are in notes at the end.

.   .   .   .

For their kindness in making the journey possible and in many other ways, I am deeply indebted to Sr. Dr. José Maria Villarreal, Colombian Ambassador in

London in 1955-56, Sir John Taylor, K.B.E., director of Canning House, Sr. Juan Guillermo Restreppo Jaramillo, Sr. Salazar Mejía and staff of the Ministerio de Agricultura, Bogotá, the late Sir George Legh-Jones and staff of the Shell Transport Coy. Ltd., and of the Shell Company of Colombia, S.A.; to Dr. Hernando Groot, Dr. Tribín, and the staff of the Instituto Roberto Franco, Villavicencio, and to Sr. General (formerly Col.) José Rafael Turriago and personnel of the Jefatura Civil y Militar de los Llanos Orientales, especially the acting commandants of the post of San Juan de Arama at the time.

For their personal friendship and hospitality I am very late in thanking J. L. Denison, Esq., Don Luis and Doña Paula Goldstein, Sr. Dr. Emiliano Borrero, and Sr. Jaime Rueda Reyes and his parents.

Contents

vii

Illustrations

between pages 96 and 97

CHAPTER I

La Macarena

THE first stop was Curaçao, which I'd sooner have missed.

The negroes passed a stony, indifferent gaze over any white—standing relaxed, but moving their eyes alone. If one asked a man where something was, he'd answer, but with a face lacking expression. The radios blared in the cafés, where soft-spoken groups of men whispered at the corner tables. They looked sour. The proprietor would talk, as it was business; then he'd lose interest and seem to be listening to the radio. One could watch the fan go round, and look at the other tourists.

At dusk the negroes sang in the streets, well and softly. They stopped as one approached, and waited till one was gone, as if they grudged the whites their music. There was little race emotion; but everywhere people were waiting for one to go. Most of them lived in smug Dutch bungalows, too neat to look convincing, and were dressed that way too.

They were enriched by a liberal and enlightened ruling class, which ran the refineries, and by the tourists. I think they learned their manners to the other race from both quarters, to use as the occasion suited.

The deserted land above Willemstad was dry and still. Fat lizards scrabbled in the bushes. The leaves were hard and spiny, hissing against my boots, and cactus sprouted from the rocks. The ground was nearly

9

snowed under in dead-white snail shells glaring in the sun, all of one kind. I felt more at home here. The way down was through silent shanties of crates and corrugated iron, where those who hadn't succeeded lived. A man came out, and showed me the way to the right part of the town, through sheer courtesy.

The streets were empty by night, except of wandering strangers, policemen, and cockroaches, which scurried along the walls under the street lamps. The air was still hot, and smelling of oil. A whip-spider was squashed on a gate, being dismembered by tiny ants. It was a dismal introduction to the tropics, where I had always wished to come.

. . . .

Beyond our wing-tips the Atlantic mountains rose through an ocean of hot air into caps of snow. We descended across green swamps, where I tried to see the alligators, to Barranquilla on the Colombian coast. Some girls in the office eased me through the formalities of entry. They smiled enchantingly at my Spanish, declared it was no trouble, and repeated everything two or three times to make sure. It was a real pleasure to misunderstand them.

Everyone was talking faster than I should have thought possible, and I couldn't make out a word of it. But people stopped me, asking how tall was I, goodness, was I English, didn't I like Colombia, of course it was home to them . . .? After Curaçao it was like a fresh drink at the end of a dusty afternoon.

Later I was told: "People on the coast talk very much."

The countryside was quiet and moist, smelling of manure. The farmers were carrying their stuff into town balanced on long poles, across their shoulders or a mule's back. I was suddenly drenched in sweat. Silken-winged butterflies floated in the shade of the hedges;

green and sapphire lizards hunted feverishly below, especially on a rubbish dump.

Along a path between the fields I caught up with a boy carrying a caged bird.

"Good afternoon." "Good afternoon, sir." "Why are you carrying the bird here?" "Yes, it's mine." He put it carefully on the ground and knelt beside it.

"Are there snakes here?" "Yes." "Are they very bad?" "Yes. It's down that road." "I wish to say, how big are the snakes?" "The airport is down there, to the left." "I know the airport's there, but the snakes are how big?" "Yes sir, big planes." He made a vague gesture with one hand, and pointed to the left.

I stayed out of the tall weeds anyway; they grew ten feet high.

My seat to Bogotá was filled by part of a merchant, who couldn't help overlapping. He spent a certain time trying to stretch the safety belt round his middle, and the rest spoiling his daughter, a surprisingly graceful dark child in white silk. We flew up a broad valley, the river braided through shadowy islands, and flooding most of the country. The comfortable merchant remarked on this to his child; I caught the word "*inundaciones*", as bits of reed huts and rafts floated down. The soil was black and tempting to farmers.

We flew through the mountains in clouds and rain, slipped over a misty ledge, and were on the plateau of Bogotá at dusk. The taxi-driver asked if I'd been here before. "Big city," he said, "big industries. Much business is done here." Neon lights shone through the rain.

The hotel was grey and silent. A morose group of impeccably dressed citizens waited in the lounge, watching some melancholy story on television, which I couldn't understand. One walked over soft grey carpets, and ate a grey expensive dinner in a nearly silent room. The few others dining made a polite murmur over their meal. The walls were painted, heavily, in scenes of the

11

region; but for this, one might have been anywhere. The service was excellent. It was too expensive to get drunk, so I went to bed.

. . . .

The hotel was a hideous modern building, set among hideous modern buildings, with gaps between where they were rebuilding to make it uglier. It was the businesslike part of town. Huge black mountains stood over it, one having a graceful white church on top, called Monserrate. In Lent, penitents went up there on their knees.

The city ended immediately beyond my hotel and I went through grass slopes into the mountain forest. A few austere yellow houses stood above the city, with wavy eucalyptus trees among them, their black leaves all drooping perpendicularly. Some rather ragged children played on the mountain road with a home-made cart, hurtling down to the bottom and dragging it up again. They asked me softly what time it was, said thank you, and went on. They were still at it three hours later, and the next day.

The woods were recently planted and entry forbidden by law. The air inside was still. No birds sang; only a cricket cheeped monotonously, like a slow clock ticking, and the leaves dripped. Yellow streams trickled down, carrying dirt from the land-slips, and the fallen leaves were sodden. Near a stream, some long chocolate-brown newts were coiled beneath a stone. They wriggled off like eels, their legs being ridiculously small for the length of body. I caught one; it was slightly moist, with the body formed in rings like a great caterpillar. Under the next stone lay some soft white eggs the size of marbles. I opened one later, and a perfectly formed baby lizard came out, pathetically new and innocent-looking. This didn't lead me anywhere.

At the edge of the mountain a cheerful chorus of

motor-horns came from the city, yet the view seemed desolate. The city plain and the low bare mountains on the horizon were bathed in an ash-grey light; and one felt as if it were the ghost of a capital, which had been buried in the dust. I don't know what inspires this feeling of unreality. One time I went with a taxi-driver who was affected the same way; he didn't seem to believe in anything till he hit it, if then. "Careful, man!" "Are you afraid?" he asked, ironically. He humoured me afterwards, avoiding everything with a comic show of care.

.   .   .   .

During the week I met a formidable entomologist, Dr Richter, who told me of a range of mountains, the Sierra de la Macarena, which means "The Hills of the Boasting Woman". I never heard who she was or what she boasted about.

Because of their steepness, and yellow fever in the monkeys, no one had ever lived there. The animals were unafraid of man. The monkeys, said Dr Richter, would sit round at a distance of two yards regarding him, I suppose, with the native solemnity of the continent; or they would imitate him trying to catch a butterfly. He had fired three times at a wild turkey in these mountains and missed because his hand was shaky with malaria. The bird had simply pecked where the bullets hit the ground, supposing them to be insects. He'd stopped firing, out of respect for its foolishness.

It would be a fine place to observe the animals, which one cannot get near when they are acquainted with the human race. I could see how they lived and what killed them when man didn't. "For example," said Dr Richter, "one can see a very curious thing there. The peccaries go in order; first the big males, then the smaller males, the females with young, and lastly the sick ones. The sickest straggle along behind, and at the rear of the troop follows a jaguar. He picks off those that lag." (It would be dangerous to attack the main body.) "So you see the jaguar is the physician of the woods."

The medical men who were with us in Dr Richter's study laughed heartily at this comparison.

It was arranged that I should go to a laboratory in Villavicencio, at the edge of the Eastern plain, to accustom myself to the country; and afterwards to the Macarena.

I returned to the mountains by night, noticing a puma skin by the roadside. Perhaps it had been killed near by: I looked round every time a caterpillar bit a leaf audibly. Though pumas are said not to attack people, they are too big to take for granted in a pitch-black forest when one hasn't a gun.

The newts were perched in low bushes of broom, hanging on to the twigs with their absurd legs, and small drab frogs kept them company, both motionless, watching for flies. The dew condensed on their skins, and dripped off their noses, but no flies came.

.   .   .   .

My plane to Villavicencio flew over harsh brown mountains shining in the early morning sun, like a landscape on the moon, and we nosed our way through the clouds at their edge. The grassland tilted away below as we wheeled: one felt like a fly settling on a map. We touched down with each wing tip brushing against a tangle of flabby-leaved vines and shrubs. The air was dank, and the light dismal. Some listless, silent men stood awaiting the plane.

I'd had no breakfast and I suppose they hadn't. Among them were a one-armed boy, and a sallow, emaciated youth, more or less paralysed, in a wheel chair: I thought them both victims of the local diseases. Only one of them was; the boy had just gone fishing with dynamite and made a mistake.

14

The bus was driven briskly through a river, round some precipices, and over a road of boulders and dust into town. It looked used to this. A thick-set man from the Institute met me, and took me to a restaurant where he knew the proprietor. "I know everyone here," he said, "they're very good people." He told his friend to fill me up, and I was given a local breakfast of steak, tomatoes, yam and black coffee. One ate the same sort of thing any time here: it was a meal. I took my coat off; then my tie. Wide, cheery men with short black whiskers came in and ate seriously, not talking much. A youth rushed in from the street with a big, pulsating sack. "Live turkey," he said urgently. They quickly came to a disagreement about the price, and the youth ran out again. Perhaps he'd stolen it; but it was usual to do business at this pace in Villavicencio.

The town was solid, busy and gleaming in the early sunlight. Well-dressed soldiers, unarmed, mixed equably with the people; a banner over the white, dusty road proclaimed: "The citizens and businesses of Villavicencio applaud the work of the civil and military head." This was probably genuine in part; he'd held office a year or two, and administered soberly and well throughout.

The principal square was green, with fountains playing, shaded by apparently ancient trees with orchids along their boughs. It was cool and immaculate, the people had pride in it.

The Institute was down by the cattle-stockades, where the road was broader, rougher, and more dusty. There was no shade. Naked brown babies crawled in a tongue of wasteland, and the houses were a little patched-up. A brown pony stood quietly tethered to the railing, while two or three small boys in oversized black sombreros practised lassoing it. Occasionally the *lazo* tipped an ear, and the pony flicked it off, while their shadows shrank into their feet.

Two tame tapirs were snoozing in the garage of the laboratory, the first I had ever seen: thick brown animals about a yard high, with long pendulous noses. We awakened them by kicking them on the bottom; scratched their stomachs for them, and spent half the morning attempting to rid ourselves of them. Monstrously fat, they were persistent beggars for food.

About noon they retired into a crackling bamboo thicket behind the laboratory. A truck drove in noisily, and two men jumped out bearing a sack of dead birds. They were an ornithologist, Dr Borrero, and the animal collector for the Institute, Carlos Velasquez. We ate lunch across the road. The eating place was made of a corrugated iron roof, with bare tables and benches, and an open fire in the corner, where the haunches of beef stood smoking. The place was popular because there was no nonsense about it.

Carlos introduced himself. "I am a Guahibo," he said. The Guahibos are an Indian tribe of notorious savagery; he was exaggerating. "I eat, smoke, drink and talk; and don't work," he remarked later. He would work full pitch up to eighteen hours a day, but this was in the same commanding manner as his talk.

"Take some of this sauce," he said, splashing it over his meat. I did. "It's good for the digestion." I told him I was burning inside. "One must accustom oneself." "When?" "In a few years." Borrero passed me his beer, to quench the flames, as he said.

After lunch, the morning's haul of birds was taken into a shed, and skinned. Some of them were mounted; Carlos assisted Borrero, and was learning the art himself very quickly, so that he could sell stuffed birds to the tourists, very dear. A woodpecker, its feathers slightly dulled in death, was mounted artistically: not too rigid, and the head at a perky angle. The next thing was to insert glass eyes, of the right shade.

CHAPTER II

Learning

AN emerald lizard about two feet long was crawling up the mango tree in the middle of the lawn. The skin was loose on its body, like chain-mail, plaited in a helmet above the neck; the eyes stared through like black pearls. At first I thought it was kept here purposely, like the tapirs. It hooked itself up among the sparse leaves and seemed to fade into them. It never appeared again.

.   .   .   .

A bunch of blue-green foothills rose over the stone wall of the Institute, rounded and crumpled like cushions left after a party. The rocks of the Cordillera had showed behind; but as I watched, hot air distilling up from the plain formed a mist over them. It became thicker and settled to the foothills, and the cloud grew out like a cotton blanket over the town. The church spire pointed to the cloud. About lunch-time the air became dark and soupy, and we waited in the shed with Borrero's birds. A few heavy drops splashed in the dust, and then a deluge. It made a noise of kettledrums on the roof. The air abruptly became cooler, and the sheets of rain glistened during lightning flashes. The tapirs enjoyed this, and trotted down to wallow in the drainage ditch.

The storm repeated itself most days of the season, between lunch and dinner. Afterwards, the puddles gleamed in a fairly gentle sun, and dried out slowly; but the air remained moist and was sopping wet at night. Water is the staff of life; so it seemed nearly anything could live here, unless something else living killed it.

We drove out to a farmer's shack and drank black coffee. They talked about hunting and wild life: *marmosas, dantas, gavilánes, colibríes, cachirres, chacurres, cafuchos, cáricáris, guaches, araguatos, cascavéles* and *tities.* "Oh yes, plenty in the stream." "What are they?" Carlos imitated an alligator with his two hands. "We just told you that, man." "I thought you said they were *chacurres.*" "No, they're a sort of hare."

There aren't any hares in Colombia.

"And what is a *cochornerría?*" Oh, they said hastily, it was just one of the words Velasquez used. His eyes gleamed and he started to explain the precise meaning, but it was rather complicated. A black and crimson butterfly, gliding in the steam from our cups, sheered off.

It was nightfall and the chickens were put away. The leaves of the banana orchard were silhouetted against the remaining light in the sky, and Carlos handed out some short black cigars. They were to repel the mosquitos, or perhaps it was to kill them—all the same, they were very good of their sort. One of the farmer's sons took me round at first, so I shouldn't get lost. He was shy, quiet anyway, and patient. We went through the bananas to a nearby river, flowing through a wood. The river was slow and oily. It glowed silver in the new moon, but too dimly to make out anything. I wore a hunter's torch, the light strapped to my forehead, so that any reflection from eyes in the growth would enter mine.

I switched it on: there were only leaves. Maybe I'd frightened everything away, but there was not even a sound. A little black frog jumped away from under my feet and I caught it. Others skittered about in the dead leaves, like as many black dice.

A pair of green sparks shone in the beam, and winked out again. The outline of a hunting spider, spanning six inches, showed in the place; it ran away lightly, in silence. The leaves remained still, and the ash-grey twigs. They were different from leaves and twigs in an English wood; more even and delicately formed.

A grasshopper sat on a shoot waving its long, slender feelers slowly forwards and back. A few big leaves drooped elegantly from the shoot, unruffled and entirely uninjured, with little beads of water along their edges. The grasshopper was alone in state on the yards of juicy foliage over our heads. It didn't eat any, but waited; probably it was a hunter. Everything remained still, as though the grasshopper were casting a spell with his antennae.

A harsh, abrupt cough sounded two or three times from the treetops behind us. The branches were faint in my torch beam; we couldn't see anything up there. The boy said it was an iguana: one of the big tree-lizards.

There were a couple of shots and we rejoined Dr Borrero and Carlos. They'd killed a pair of tree-rats: it was these which coughed in the rising moon.

We went down a long track to a meadow, where a kind of huge swimming rodent, the capybara, some-times came out, but not this time. My snake-proof boots sploshing in the puddles would have been sufficient to stop them anyway.

When we returned, one of the tapirs had been sleeping on Borrero's bed, leaving it rather bent and muddy, with an enormous bloodstained puddle along-side. We opened bottles of soft drink and studied the phenomenon. It showed the tapir was thoroughly domesticated, and had some kidney disease. As Borrero observed, an ordinary flesh wound would have bled everywhere—not only in the puddle. I ought really to have shut the door when we left.

We went to bed, Borrero in his hammock, because I didn't know how to sleep in one and he did.

.   .   .   .

It rained and Borrero worked on his specimens. "This is the punishment for hunting." The skins were thin and the feathers easily sullied; and the bones had to be severed through an incision in the wing-tip.

"These herons came from Africa twenty years ago. They eat the ticks in the cattle pastures." These were pure white birds about half a yard long. "This flies close to the ground with its mouth open, and the insects go in." It was a great downy speckled bird with a soft, wide bill, like an overgrown chick.

Carlos came in to clean his gun and help Borrero. I was opening the skinned birds, to learn their diet and parasites. "Dirty work," he said. It was dark and raining outside; a few house flies revolved listlessly over our heads and a heavy-bodied spider prowled on the window pane. "It stinks, *guaputas*." The odour came from my dissections.

"*Putas* [whores] I know: why *gua*putas?" I meant that I understood the word.

"How many *guaputas* do you know?"

One had to speak accurately.

This was when I learnt the names of the animals. Next door an anaconda of twelve feet was coiled in a dead branch, the coils slipping now and then, and rubbing against the wire of the cage. There were opossums; scaly armadillos scrabbling for bits of food under the doors of their hutches; rats and monkeys.

Outside, frogs clung to the buildings in the morning, or after rain. They flattened their white skins against the wall and looked like frog-shaped blobs of whitewash. They could change colour as rapidly as a chameleon, matching any shade except a blue or red. One of them sat on a wall, and seeing only the painted door-frame, showed up in the same bright green, as if the painter had done it for a joke.

Carlos and his friends showed me the peccaries kept in a cage, grunting cheerfully, friendly behind the wire; a frog as big as a rat ejecting what they said was poison through its rear, but safe to touch; a hairy wasp with no wings, chequered like a draughtboard, said to be worse than a scorpion; a glittering green one the size of an English hornet which they caught in a handkerchief, three small harmless snakes and a vast butterfly. Its wings were like a night sky on top, and the eyes of an owl beneath; it was battered and worn with age, beating tremulously against the window.

"*Marisopla*," said Carlos.

"*Mariposa.*" The name suited its indolent flight in the still air. Besides I wasn't going to be had on such an ordinary word.

"Ah! I told you incorrectly so you'd get it right for a change."

In the sun, the rubbish heap behind the laboratory was afire with butterflies. Several kinds were of the same pattern, striped orange, yellow and black along the veins: some of them unpleasant for birds to eat, and so alike a bird need only have learnt the pattern once. This is already well known.

In the end I got all the names right and could talk as convincingly about the animals as any plainsman. Besides, they told me the fine arts of living in the forest: how to know if peccary meat was wormy, or kill warble-fly maggots under the skin. Borrero showed me the disadvantages of scratching fly bites: little permanent black spots.

I heard of the trees that raise blisters big as eggs if one stands near them; of the times the peccaries run through the town; of bird-eating spiders and scorpions, and of an anaconda thirty-nine feet long.

A merchant I met had this snake somewhere about and wanted fluid to preserve the skin before he killed it. He hadn't known that I was interested in snakes, but would sell it to me, and alive, if I preferred. Only he'd have to pay some men to bring it round. He certainly would. I never saw him again. He was a smallish man with a very neat moustache.

.   .   .   .

A long white plume of dust rolled into the fields behind us. A dead mule lay on the verge, stinking and covered with thirsty butterflies, while the vultures sat in an orderly line alongside, resting between meals. It would have made a good petrol advertisement, for the mule was entirely caved-in.

The fields were newly cut from forest here, while vines, spiky shrubs and low, floppy-leaved trees spread over the old ones. The dead stems of palms, that had been too hard to cut, stuck out high above, with a grey hawk on top, watching. We'd stop while Borrero and Velasquez discussed if it was a species they wanted. The tick-eating herons wheeled across like huge snowflakes, vanishing over the woods.

Velasquez asked for his cartridge belt: "Throw out the buggery, ——it, please," and moved slowly with Borrero after the hawk. The field vibrated from the sound of grasshoppers. Velasquez would stand under the palm impassively. The bird might fly away, but if he fired it dropped like a wet rag; and he was dissatisfied if it even squeaked. They'd come back silent, or somewhat annoyed, and wait for a while smoking. Swallow-tail butterflies swooped along the road between patches of mud.

It seemed the less natural the country, the more animals in it. A kind of thickly-built spider prowled in the fields like a miniature leopard. It crept up on a fly or cricket, each leg snapping forward to escape notice, and paused. The eyes gleamed; and it would pounce. There were glossy lizards behaving exactly the same way. Many times over, almost the same hunter killed nearly the same victim.

We drove into a remaining strip of woodland, like a green chasm forty yards high each side of the road. A patchy curtain of creepers hung down from the trees and the sunlight slanted into it ten or twenty feet up. A few little dragonflies circled there. Herons and parrots flew over the top occasionally, squawking.

This was what I wanted: to see the animals living in their natural place. Inside there'd be caterpillars galore, from which I could breed such beautiful butterflies as I had seen in the Institute. They'd told me there were no snails, because there was too little lime in the soil for them to make shells; but there'd be numerous slugs. There'd be stick insects and leaf insects, very difficult to see; and dead logs seething with termites. Up in the trees, sloths, monkeys, iguanas and ant-bears would be climbing; deadly tree-vipers would be curled round the twigs, and gorgeously coloured tree-frogs hopping in the leaves. Not to speak of the puma, jaguar or fer-de-lance snake: one might not see them first time. I listened for the stir and rustling.

There wasn't a sound. We crept beneath the vines. The air was still and clean as cut glass, so that the filtered shafts of sunlight didn't show in it. One's hand was suddenly lit up as one stretched it out. The shadows were a watery transparent grey: one could see clearly in every direction.

A silent brown bird, like a thrush with clipped wing-tips, fluttered clumsily to one side through a space. I supposed that all the life was hidden, and cut up the dead logs and sticks. There were brown crickets in some of the hollow sticks; they crawled out, waving their long feelers, and bit me.

It gave me a doubtful kind of affection for them. They kicked against my hand with their spiny legs; that was how living things ought to behave. The leaves all around were smooth-edged, elegant and crisp: nothing rustled them and nothing ate them, or ever had. They depressed me, like laurels. It wasn't particularly hot, but I felt very tired.

At the end of the wood there was a big hole, surrounded by excavated golden earth. A buzz like a distant plane came behind my shoulder and a humming-bird hovered there. It flashed bronze, and disappeared entirely; the noise passed through the leaves. I fetched Velasquez and asked him what kind of animal made the hole. "Ants," he said.

It became dark, and a little cooler; back on the road it was evening, about five-thirty. The sun shone along the road from a greenish west sky. Carlos and Borrero introduced me to the local animals. "Look," they said, "a night-monkey in the crook of that tree staring at you." The tree was big and twisted, shaded by creepers, and the monkeys crept into a hole without my seeing them. There weren't any more.

We drove on to a farmer they knew, living in a house of bamboo and thatch. It was dusk and spiders crept up the wall to hunt. We drank coffee and set out as before. Borrero smoked the rustic black cigar with a scholar's appreciation: "At home I always smoke cigarettes; but cigars are best in the woods, and strong ones at that." He looked casually into the wickerwork of branches, a hundred feet up and far off, holding a thin spray of leaves against the evening sky. He puffed his cigar for a while. "Look, an iguana. It's walking along that branch." One of the twigs seemed to wave slightly.

There was the note of a bird, and Borrero faded into the undergrowth in the direction it came from. "Good luck, then," he said. He trod on a twig, used a very uncultivated word under his breath, and was gone.

The forest was no different, but I found more. My face stung and my shins itched for a start; something was getting at me. It was some little flies, too small to be seen by torchlight. I rubbed myself with a cool, glossy leaf like a waterlily's to soothe the bites. There was a little net-like pattern in part of the leaf, where some insect had gnawed it away.

The leaf-medicine wasn't much good; but other leaves of this sort had occasionally a similar scar, in the same place. It was interesting: they never had any other kind, and only they ever had this one. I began to look for scars in all the leaves. There weren't many, but in every kind which was ever scarred, the same rule was true, with one exception. Something bit semicircular pieces, the size of half a ha'penny, out of several different leaves. They were scalloped with these bites all the way down the sides.

A little dew formed, and I was very tired. I looked at a tree carefully, being frightened of anything I might not see, and leaned against it. It was a great surprise: my hand was stung as if the bark were full of red-hot needles. Scores of slim brown ants had come through little holes from inside the tree. They raced everywhere like dust in a whirlwind, pursuing what might have been an insect they could have caught. At least, that's how it seemed.

Further on stood a thin white sapling, with the same little ants racing all over it, without my touching. They were there when I turned the torch on.

There was nothing else to be seen. I joined Carlos, who gave me a cigarette. He'd killed nothing, because whatever he'd found was not needed. He wouldn't say what he had seen. "A few animals." He'd caught a little harmless brown snake for me. I showed him a scalloped-out leaf. "Ants," he said. "Like those which make the hole in the ground."

. . . .

The truck broke down, and I went off to wait in a clearing. There were few midges, so one could keep still. An owl hooted in the distance; I turned the torch on, but there was nothing there. It was quiet for an hour; then, when I turned the torch on again, the silvery eyes of an owl shone at me from a low branch. Borrero might have wanted it, and I'd killed nothing. They probably didn't think I could, so I took careful aim at its neck and fired. The owl toppled over and three dancing green eyes appeared from behind it. They were little chestnut opossums skipping along the twigs, their pointed noses quivering with fear.

The owl had fallen into a stream, but struggled out again. I couldn't find it. At least I'd been harmless up to then.

I felt cold driving home, but immediately we stopped the air was like a blanket. We dumped our specimens in the laboratory: Borrero had killed a few birds. It seemed a pity, but there were strict rules. "If one kills to eat, or for knowledge," said Carlos, "it's permissible. But one must do it well. To kill for no reason or make a wound and lose the animal is a mortal sin."

An endless chain of semicircular bits of leaves hurried along the path outside, in the light of a window. I followed them across the lawn and picked one up; an angular brown ant hung on to it by her jaws. These were the leaf-cutter ants, whose work we had seen in the woods. They were more numerous here.

. . . .

CHAPTER II. PART 2

We were in Velasquez's house. The room was bare and clean, half-shuttered, and a light bulb gleamed on the beer bottles. Most of the pets, including a biggish anaconda in the backyard, were sound asleep, but a stilt-legged bird stalked about cheeping musically for crumbs, and a parrot nibbled my ear.

I was told a man needed a certain delicacy in hunting. "Well, I walk as quietly as I can, and the boots keep the flies from biting my legs like that." Velasquez was bathing Borrero's ankles with a herbal lotion he had concocted.

"Without offence, you sound like the escape of a wounded tapir. And the flies didn't make this stinking mess, but scratching it." "Thank you," said Dr Borrero. "Not at all, Doctor." He swabbed some more stuff on.

His children were coaxed to sleep peacefully in a dark corner, and the young wife came over to us without embarrassment, joining in the beer and teasing Carlos sometimes, a very difficult thing to manage. She looked at my boots demurely and said: "How very big." Well, they protected me from snakes. "Surely," said Borrero, "for all the animals are frightened away in advance." Carlos simulated a monkey hugging the treetops, pop-eyed with fright.

I bought some tennis shoes, but they made little difference either way. I came across no poisonous snake, and the forest life I had imagined didn't exist.

Dead leaves fell occasionally, just covering the ground. One of them was like a delicate fan of lace: its whole blade had been eaten, but all the veins preserved. I looked patiently, and found two more like it. No more of the fresh litter had been eaten at all. There could be few creatures in the trees, unless feeding entirely on the bark.

A spider on a drooping palm-frond opened its fangs at me, like hooks for trout. It needed to be fierce: it wouldn't catch anything for days. I resisted the impulse to pat its head, and passed on. However, the others had killed a young tapir for the Museum.

A zoologist from Bogotá joined us, with a wide flat mouth, solemn manner, large ears, long arms and straight red hair. He was usually called "Monkey"; one might have suspected the same deep irreverence. We all went out together.

Carlos shouted a kind of compliment to some girl by the road, who stiffened and glared back at us as the dust obscured her. There was a short silence till we drew breath cautiously a hundred feet past the dead mule; and the vultures returned to their work. It was past time.

I don't know if the shoes improved my hunting. Carlos said: "Fine. Now you can give me the boots. They're very good; and if I and my wife quarrel we can sleep in them separately." It wasn't likely.

Occasionally some creature stirred suddenly or appeared on a leaf where it hadn't been before. It was always a new kind: a lizard with long back legs, that leapt like a frog; a fluffy little bird-eating spider in a silk tunnel; a wasp shaped like a goblet making a flask of mud; a heavy-jowled rat in a tree.

Their movements were sharp, unhesitating and practised, like those of tradesmen in some unique and exacting craft. Obviously the animals that fed on the leaves were like that too, because of the scars. It is said that creatures are forced into these strict ways of life when there is a crowded struggle between them. The kind that lives best in a certain place is apt to be that which lives nowhere else. It thrives, and so do the hunting animals and parasites that feed specially on it. The living there will be too meagre and dangerous for anything else. The forest would be tattered, with a pair of jaws in every shadow.

I missed a lot, for the others brought in a climbing ant-eater, a rat, an opossum and several birds in ten nights. While I chopped up a rotten log, perhaps some animal was concealed in the open veil of shade around it. Yet the leaves had shown plainly that there was little feeding on them. It was as quiet as it seemed.

Carlos said he had nearly killed me wandering between him and a rat. "You would not have fired by mistake." "No, but on purpose."

Our last night there was a brilliant moon and nothing stirred. I came back disconsolate to the lorry, chilled by the dew and itching. For an hour or so I tried to sleep, disturbed by conscience for having no specimens, and by a few late mosquitoes. Then the others returned empty-handed, to my delight. We spoke little and loaded the guns in the back. A tree-rat coughed sharply in the tree immediately above us. Borrero looked into the branches for a moment without speaking. "Your mother . . ." he observed softly, and we went home.

. . . .

I killed one or two frogs and reptiles to preserve. The prescribed method for them was to drop nicotine in the nostrils, yet the little snake wriggled round the cage as if to escape something painful; and the frogs tried to wipe it from their noses. They took several seconds to die. It proved best to put them in a polythene bag with an open cyanide bottle; they went off without a quiver.

A dead animal is a document of its life, perhaps a complete one, but very little of it can be read. I'd learnt nothing from them while alive; for they had been numb with fright, preoccupied in getting out, or fatally passive. At best they could only have become more skilful in being kept, settled in their habits, and lazy. Whatever lived in the woods was only there.

. . . .

The doctors gave an annual party, to which everybody in a biological profession in the plain came. The jokes, talk and whisky were as good as they would have been at a similar reunion in Scotland, but it was more musical. Two of the drunkest gave an entrancing and poetical song from Antioquía, a highland region, to their own complex guitar accompaniment, and the sweat poured down their brows. The host had a swimming pool; we dipped in and out, ate sucking pig, and were caught in a sudden torrent of rain.

We talked on the veranda: "His ranch was here. The river changed course a mile, took it away, and went back. He bought another and the same thing happened. He never goes to wash now because the river doesn't like him. Says it might drown him some day. They're superstitious." One could see the point though.

"There is plenty of game out East but the parasites don't matter. It's drier and the eggs die in the grass. They keep the cows out of the woods but it doesn't make any difference if they do go in." "We put down D.D.T. and the carriers died."

"It's water from a village pond. Contains an astronomical quantity of amoebas." The amoebas would give one dysentery if one wasn't exposed to them already. This was a tough old man handing round a dark green bottle. People tried it hopefully and were disgusted. Then he explained, for they all took pleasure in experiments and in effects of nature.

The party ended at four with little hesitation. They said to one another: "So long, then," and started back to their practices, in Villavicencio or way beyond. We had tea with the Spanish director of a sanatorium, married to an English lady. It was quiet and agreeable; there weren't many patients. The Señora hadn't been home since marrying and didn't much want to. We talked only of this place and the possible opportunities.

The day ended as the party had; the sun went down at six, as always, a blue-green tint remained in the sky briefly, and it was night. We ate supper in the shack by the stockades, with the owner, who was drinking to celebrate his birthday. "I had a very good restaurant in town. Shaved every day; clean tablecloths. I made little. In this place there is no tablecloth. I shave on Sunday before Mass. This is much better, you see. It's the same food for the same money, but one feels easy here."

.   .   .   .

We ate up town the next day, for a change. The road was muddy and the people who had to go out wore *ruanas*, square wool blankets with a square hole in the middle, the rain streaming from the folds. Carlos treated the waitress, passing the time at our table, to an absurdly long, level stare, without speaking. She couldn't sit looking unconcerned for ever. "One of my girl friends," he said. We remarked on his lack of decorum, but he was aware of it.

The restaurant was bare and gaunt. Four grizzled men sat next to us, not talking. They had taken some weeks riding in from the plain, and forty empty beer bottles stood in a neat square between them. We didn't disturb them.

"Very hospitable, though cautious at first. One must be tactful with them." "In the plain one lives on what is there. You ask the way somewhere; plainsman tells you: 'It's across the second river and three days to the east.' What if you're lost? He says there are plenty of vultures and armadillos—you won't be. He means, you can eat them: you're not lost till you starve."

They liked to say: "We don't make money, but we enjoy life." The market was far, the land and roads were bad, and it wouldn't pay to improve them. They would never be rich in votes, if they voted, and still less in money. This was quite obvious, and the Turkish immigrants here and there, who grew rich behind shop counters, just amused the plainsmen. They had their horses, apropos of which they said:

"A brown nostril doesn't matter, so long as it breathes."

However, Carlos said that most of them told lies. "Once I kept a family of rattlesnakes, for curiosity. The first year they made two rings each time they moulted, and one twice a year afterwards. But the plainsmen say there are rattlesnakes of ten or twelve years, because there are that many rings."

"If you don't see a thing, and there are no traces, don't believe it."

CHAPTER III

Don Alicio's Land

VELASQUEZ had a friend, Don Alicio, the master of a ranch beyond San Martín in the plain, who invited us to stay and hunt with him. We were eight or nine persons, counting Carlos's children, and the talk went too fast for me to follow. "Eh, Mister," shouted a neat little man in a gleaming shirt. I hadn't seen him before and didn't wish to. The "Mister" implied that I was not only English, which is all right, but too complacent even to know I was being got at. "It's good in the plain," he yelled. He was a windbag, who'd as soon have been playing billiards in a Villavicencio café.

It was a warm day, coming on to rain; we had several beers at a grocery under the mountains. The air was sticky, and it grew dark outside. A huge wasp, shining like dark-blue coal, entered fanning the dust over the floor with her wing-beat. She searched for bird-eating spiders' holes and boomed off into the tepid rain. The talk resumed: "I knew a Turk, who told me he had nine children. 'Four little Moslems and five accidentally'."

The rain usually piled up against the mountains; and as far as we had yet gone, it was nearly always wet. Further out, the endless grass began. San Martín faced the grassland, and Creole ponies waited casually in the street, as if the old Spanish houses belonged to them. The square was shaded with fountains and flower beds, but nobody walked in it. Perhaps there was a time for going there. We loaded with lemonade for the next day's heat. There was a little traditional finery in the store but mostly rough working goods; and the trading price for peccary skins was chalked up in a corner.

The grass rolled out into a dark haze. We rattled along two white bands of dry soil, scaring the lanky prairie birds over the grass. They whistled peevishly, with a plaintive dying fall as they were obscured.

"Very delicious, the air," said Borrero. It seemed a bit chilly. We came to a wood rising in a flattened dome directly from the savannah. It was like a park, but with no fences, and deserted. The eyes of small owls shone at us every few hundred yards, fixed in the road. They floated off as we came to them and alighted at the same point behind, staring back.

The grass shone pale grey under the stars, and the woods appeared like villages out to the horizon. A dog barked, and we drew up. Don Alicio's ranch was a wide roof on wooden supports. It was far off the track and the dog provided enough security. He quietened it in a low voice and introduced his family and one or two ranch-hands. Carlos and he said: "We're acquainted," embraced, and started telling each other a number of lies.

We slung our hammocks to the beams and ate a stew of peccary, tasty meat, but excessively tough. The hearts were tender; I picked one up. Carlos said urgently: "Don't eat it; it's poisonous. A Christian doesn't eat them. . . . Thanks, very delicious." There was little conversation; the plainsmen hadn't the habit of talking anyway, and bits of peccary kept sticking in our teeth.

We went off to hunt separately. The woods were clearer than at Villavicencio, and the trees rose higher in the middle, where the ground sloped abruptly to a crystal brook or a spring.

Only little moths flew through them, with tufts of blue-grey hair on their tails. They gathered on me to drink the sweat, settled on the torch, throwing horrifying shadows ahead, and tickled inside my shirt. It seemed I was too smelly, as I attracted these moths, and too noisy attempting to keep them out of my trousers, for a jaguar not to notice me. Don Alicio had said there were a few in the region.

I lay in a bay of grass, next to a further wood, watching the dew condense on my gun. During an hour there was no sound, and then a sudden, fiendish squealing and grunting: peccaries obviously. They said that peccaries would leave your shoes behind, or at any rates the soles; enough to bury. The noise ran round the wood and died away, and my scalp settled.

The ranch light was out, but I knew the constellation of Orion and remembered that the sword points north. It doesn't, so I was lost for four hours. Then I tried the opposite idea, and returned at the same time as Borrero. It was an escape, not from peccaries or a jaguar, but from the distance.

Borrero had found nothing. We drank some *aguardiente* of his with lemonade in alternate swigs, smoking his cigars. He said the noise I'd heard had probably been wild turkeys. This was true: I saw them doing it later. Perhaps they frighten anything that would eat them straight up a tree; they can also hush, and seem to have passed beyond earshot. "You're beginning to fit in," he said, looking through the *aguardiente* bottle with a torch. "We'll keep some for tomorrow."

The air flowing over the grass at night was fresh, and smelled sweet.

.   .   .   .

Dragonflies and glossy indigo wasps darted across the plain in the morning, before the dew had boiled off. The Señora yelled for the dog and it raced into the cookhouse snapping and snarling, to frighten the pigs away. We chewed dry salted beef for breakfast, gloomily, and began arranging a hunt.

35

The grass outside began to look wiry; the light pressed the colours from it and blackened the woods. Don Alicio talked lazily and slowly over our prospects. Were there alligators in the lake? "Those underneath rotting." Anacondas? "They stay in the water. My wife killed one here a month back. Measured eighteen feet . . . she was washing clothes in the brook and had to cut its head off."

A toucan flapped slowly from one wood to the next, Borrero following. It glanced along his gun barrel, at a hundred paces, and went into the trees. The air quivered over the horizon and Borrero returned, hot though amused. I felt that I'd learned something, though it was uncertain what. It had something to do with the woods.

Our truck joggled over termites' nests, like concrete pots in the dry grass. The lake gleamed in a ring of flat-topped hills, sharply cleft down from a common height. Gigantic white cranes stood in the shallows. They cackled at our approach, opened their broad wings and beat up one by one to the far end. There was a murmur in the forest encircling the lake. "Turkeys," said the Colombians. As we drew near it became totally quiet. I went off looking for anacondas, not to impede the hunting.

We returned five hours later. "What did you see?" "A great black bird; don't know what it was." What they had found was an alligator; they brought in a yard of its tail. Boiled for dinner it was like fish, but rubbery, with heavy, rounded bones. The bird had been a turkey. I'd seen it on a grey branch in a swamp; and it had flown off before I was certain of the distance. "*Ojalá*," murmured the Colombians, expressing their regret tactfully.

Apart from the turkey, there had been a long green gourd, precisely like a tree-viper: head, tail, scales and serpentine bend. When I noosed it the head snapped, and I understood why it hadn't wriggled. It had been in a dark place over a stream.

That night they talked over the past, with pauses. It was too serious for this kind of book. Perhaps it was progress. there were classes of newly powerful rich men and managers, and of confused or dispossessed poor, not here but in the highlands. In 1948 a leader of the dispossessed had been murdered, perhaps accidentally, and social war began, becoming a struggle for life itself. It spread into the plain, though the plainsmen probably had little quarrel with one another; and nearly everything had been destroyed. Don Alicio had owned a house in San Martín, and seventy head of cattle. There was an old man on the ranch, who'd been richer, and whose family had been killed as well. But Alicio had been able to start again; he'd bred a stock of twenty head, built the house and cleared the wood below to plant coffee; and his wife had raised their children. This time they were far from civilization.

"The bands came from the Cordillera, and if the people weren't with them, they killed everyone and burned the houses." "Which side?" "It made no difference . . ." "The people were dead."

Don Alicio paused. "The land will hold five hundred cattle and perhaps I could get a new house." He didn't want one much, but his wife would prefer it. There was no floor and the hogs came in.

He had held their baby in his arms while his wife was still cooking. "*Hijo, hijo,*" he murmured: a son.

.   .   .   .

The further wood gave out a low resonant noise at night and in the morning, like a gale in the mountains, or heavy seas at a distant beach. It was howler monkeys chanting, probably to keep the wood for their own.

They were silent after the sun had risen and the blue-green faded from the grass. There were supposed to be peccaries about, thought it was uncertain where they'd be hiding this morning. We closed in through one of the woods without success, and hunted casually in others.

Each of these black islands concealed a pocket in the land, for the highest trees grew on the bottom, where the stream ran. They were graceful pillars of ash-grey, springing through the dark green veil of lower trees into the sun.

There was a delicate patter on the leaves, and a little black animal appeared behind a low palm. It had crinkly pink ears and a flat-ended snout. It heard me move, and bounded away. I never learned what it had been, and probably it was edible too; one could have kept the skin.

In the afternoon, where the howlers had been, a dozen little grey-green monkeys danced along the upper boughs, one by one. They shook twigs and bits of bark into the trees below, giving them away in the silence. I shot the last one, and it fell heavily, but screamed like a baby before I could despatch it. This was a death-noise, which would give the rest of the troop a horror of humans, for they saw me. Two of them faced down and imitated the call, before running off. There was no trace of the howlers.

The little monkey was full of thin translucent worms; and there might have been yellow fever virus in its blood, but I don't think we got a good sample of it, back at the ranch. "You have slain a wild beast in the jungle," they said.

"Exactly!"

The howling monkeys called again after dark. It was a little mysterious how they had got there, since the wood had been isolated for centuries. Maybe they wandered through the savannah at night. We bathed in the icy brook below the ranch, on silvery sand, with no anacondas about.

"Did you like the water?" asked a plainsman. "People enjoy themselves here." He was silent for a while. "They say a pilot came down and stayed. It would have been some years ago. Maybe he's still there. He stayed because he liked it."

Slender greenish insects walked in and swayed in front of the lamp, on an upturned crate. They looked like pieces of the grass outside, in every detail. It must have been ancient to have bred creatures so similar to it. Their front legs were long and sharp; and one of them lashed out at a pale green cockroach, but it got away.

.   .   .   .

The streams joined in a swift river, brilliantly clear and delicious to swim in. The slim, wiry boughs arched high over it, and trailed their vines in the water; we could hold on to them and swing against the current. The sun glanced through the middle and lighted the sand underneath. We swam without care.

It was different wading. "One can poke in front with a stick where there is sand. I used to think this too inconvenient, but a ray stung me here three months ago." This was a friend of Alicio's, a doctor in San Martín. "The ray buries itself, but moves if one pokes it, so one doesn't step on them. So it's better to use the stick. The venom is very interesting." It had burned till the next day, and the mark now on his ankle was like an ink blotch the size of a hand. He was still lame.

Don Alicio's children cut sharp stakes from a palm frond, which they played with as spears, and trailed silently behind their father into the forest. It was dark inside, with spidery twigs and vine-stems, but airy and clean.

A jaguar had drunk from the river, leaving clear prints. It was going to inspect Alberto, our driver, that afternoon, from ten feet away, scenting him. "I was waiting for Carlos. Heard a noise in front and called him. No answer. There was a little noise at my side. Called again. Then behind me. *Mierda,* I thought.

There was a leaf quivering. Then Carlos came and I thought he'd been playing a trick. But we found the tracks in a circle." The rest of us weren't concerned to hear this. The jaguar just killed its food: "If it's not hungry, the animals don't trouble; nor do we, for it doesn't eat people." It was phlegmatic and calm.

Indeed, a jaguar and the zoologist we called Monkey saw each other this afternoon—and it's very rare for one to be seen—and even he didn't unnerve it. This was probably the same beast, slipping like a gentle breeze over the brown leaves we trod. It may have noted three zoologists.

Intensely coloured butterflies, small and slightly built, gleamed like chips of stained glass in the shade. I heard only one sound, an unending hiss from the forest floor. It wasn't a snake. A close army of termites were marching through the shadows, each rapping its head against the dry leaves. Ten or twenty thousand vibrated their heads, in a column of some yards. Perhaps it kept them in rank or frightened the birds, but that wasn't important, even if it were true. They were marching openly and by day through the woods, which was strange, and this seemed to incite them to their midget drum-beat.

I moved quietly enough to kill a chestnut heron, for the skin and for supper. But Carlos and Alberto emerged with three peccaries on a pole, trussed with vines. Carlos was matter-of-fact; Alberto wildly excited.

I helped them through the rushes at the end; we loaded the corpses in the truck and stood smoking in the sun. The wasps crawled over my arms and hands drinking the sweat. Looking at the solid ivy-green wall of the forest, I could see what had escaped me before. The trees were centred on water, but advanced into the dry ground, or retreated from it, with an ordered front. They stood together in their own shade. On the smaller woods, the nearly even roofs of foliage covering the

40

stream-beds also kept the streams from the sun. Inside, it was always unruffled and still, with the few long leaves standing out in a precise order from their slightly drooping twigs. If anything moved, it was always unique in its kind. Even a cockroach was stamped by the forest, as though it had been patterned in some weird seed-case.

The forest appeared as a single being, cool and controlled within, and keeping itself whole. One had to see the wall to believe this. At Villavicencio, only fragments of the forest were left, and it had seemed uncanny, like a hydra surviving in pieces.

Black inside, the fondness of the insects for our sweat became a nuisance. Tiny bees, disregarding slaps, curses and cigarette smoke, swarmed over one thickly. Anyway, they couldn't sting, and we were drugged by the wind and sun. When the midges came out, we dipped once or twice in the river to confuse them by drowning our odour; and quit.

There was rain in the night, but I didn't hear it. The morning was dry, with the grey-brown thatch and timbers of the ranch-house gleaming dully in a heavy sun. The shade of the roof seemed a solid block. A few chickens and lizards scrabbled in the yard behind the cookhouse as we ate our peccary for breakfast. One of them pursued a cherry-red dragonfly, which took off and clicked its wings in the sun. The ranch-hands ate silently and rode away.

We said goodbye. One of the hands remarked to me, "Don't let the jaguars devour you in the Macarena." Everybody shook with laughter, and we went.

On the journey I tried feeding bananas to a toucan Borrero had winged that morning. Its eyes were clear in the sky-blue skin, and its feathers bright, but it wouldn't feed or drink. It wanted to get at my fingers before its own time came.

We came under the mountains and a high cloud. Tick-eating herons walked about the bullocks and even

41

sat on them. The cattle glanced up at Borrero, stalking the herons across a field, and ambled away as he fired. The wet ground deadened the air above, and seemed better for diseases than cattle; but it made them calm. Don Alicio's beasts were seldom injured, except trying to jump the corral; while these ones stayed within a dilapidated fence.

It grew dark, and the buildings of the Institute were a dismal grey. Borrero assembled his scores of glossy bird skins, unnaturally bright against the stone floor. "Big killing." "Shame," he replied. But without having a collection, one couldn't tell what was there. "They look brilliant, but I suppose the same colours are in the forest, and one doesn't notice. For it's difficult to see them. Also, the species are scarce, and one comes across them only by luck, some day."

He'd told me before, but I hadn't believed him then. It was true, and not only of the birds. The leaf of a certain tree had touched me on one of our earlier hunts, raising a welt like a whiplash. It had burned on my neck for a few hours. When going through leaves afterwards, I'd expected a second burn, for it gave one no immunity. I didn't know the shape, but the leaf hadn't touched me since.

We had a bottle of rum, and collected in the living-room to drink Borrero's farewell. The room depressed us, and the little paper cups seemed contemptible. Our guest came too late from the laboratory. "Very kind thought," he said, and returned later with a new bottle. Carlos cleaned his gun, which I'd held on the journey. He found the barrel was a little scratched. "Don Stéban," he said courteously, "you have soiled the sodomitery, debauch it!" The rum, named after the botanist Caldas, who was shot by Spanish forces in 1816, burned with a merry blue flame on a piece of cotton wool.

CHAPTER IV

Organization

IT was the dry season; no clouds formed by day and the sky shone peacock blue after sundown. The young men put on their whitest shirts in the dusk and strolled, apparently without aim, in the main street, occasionally breaking off for an ice. The girls went by giggling at one another. I was out of this, not intending to settle there. The scented air, the inviting twilight and the café music just made me melancholy.

Nearly everything was excited. The grasshoppers hatched and swarmed over the lawn of the Institute; a hundred kinds of butterfly danced in the air and chivvied each other. A brown hawk-moth, eight inches wide, flew with perfect self-possession just above the dirt road, weaving among the legs of the people. It turned into a shop, seeking the dark, and swooped up suddenly round the head of the girl behind the counter. She screamed a bit and attempted to beat it away. Perhaps she was wearing scent.

A species of flat water-scorpion, big as a man's hand, with six powerful hooked legs and leathery wings, crept out of the ditches by night and flapped about the street lamps. One or two were squashed on a wall in the morning, resembling devils in a medieval picture of Hell.

The people went out to celebrate the opening of a ford, where we'd been hunting. There were stalls cooking meat and selling beer in a dirt space cleared below the trees; the men sat along the benches drinking, practical-

43

ly silent. "I'm going." "So long, then." It was a political occasion, intended to arouse enthusiasm.

Monkey and I bathed from a wire cableway strung over a deep. "You missed an anaconda," he said, having shaken me in from the bank. "It fell into the water from that branch when you splashed. A little one, not two yards."

A lorry got stuck across the ford: the men came to life, and ran to pull it out, joking and flashing their teeth. "Gee up." "Stop." "Listen, it's drowning already." The machine gurgled. "Pull harder, man." "Your grandmother. You pull." "No point; you're stronger than I."

They dragged it into the sun, and settled down again to the beer. Two old enemies had an argument in the space, striking each other, but we didn't concern ourselves. Their friends went to stop it. "They're both fools, the one and the other." "But they have only their hands." It had to be stopped even so, since neither would have accepted defeat permanently.

The lorries raced one another back at sundown to get ahead of the dust. We stayed out late, wandering from Carlos's home round the drab and democratic cafés. Everyone wore two days' stubble and a white shirt, shook hands and paid for a round, though some of them were quite rich.

We moved downtown. "Look," said Carlos. "Whores. Very good." Alberto could no longer walk, but he drove correctly with a frown, sweating all over his face. We drank as the only guests at a certain house, trying to provoke Alberto to dance. "Can't. Let's have some beer." Each side teased the other quietly and decorously, to pass the time. The women were better-bred in their conversation than the sheltered girls uptown, and more lively; Carlos for some reason was courteous with them. We paid as if indifferent to the prices; I copied the other two with difficulty.

44

At the end I danced with an amused girl half my height, and Alberto laughed so much after, he drove into a pothole. It was midnight and the steam rose into the cool air over a sausage stand. We munched some, while heavily-armed policemen went about closing the places down, perhaps in case of disorders. Carlos made a fiercely indiscreet remark and we left.

.　　.　　.　　.　　.　　.　　.　　.　　.　　.　　.　　.

I felt more in place by day, with business to do. It seemed I needed at least five men for a journey into the Macarena, and all kinds of medicines and armaments. However, the people who told me so had never been there. Dr Richter, of the University in Bogotá, had told me he often went for a quiet vacation—with a man to do the cooking, because he'd lost a hand in the First World War. "It's quite safe unless one drowns in the river."

It was a question of temperament partly. Richter never took medicines, and bathed among *caribes*, the saw-toothed fish that attack at the smell of blood, in shoals. "Provided one isn't bleeding . . . Besides, in the Macarena, they're only in the south."

I had once asked Borrero how Dr Richter had lived so long. "We all wonder. But if he's not killed the way he drives in Bogotá, he won't die."

I had to go light anyway. It was fortunate, for in fact two men are safer than ten in the forest. The ten would starve. Carlos was needed by the Institute, but a friend of his came the morning after our party.

"Rafael Restrepo. They told me you wanted to go to the Macarena." He was about thirty-five, reserved and indestructible as a rock. We sat outside, talking obliquely. He happened to have been there on two expeditions. Yes, it was pleasant. One would be hunting and might find something valuable there? Perhaps. It turned out that he was free to come. I had already agreed to a certain wage with Carlos, and Rafael would not have taken less or asked more. He was a professional; the expedition existed.

We needed stores at commissariat prices, a gun licence, the gun itself and ammunition, tents, hammocks, tools and an air passage towards the Macarena. It would have been difficult, but there was an army.

It had been the sole political power since the social war. If there had been social fighting among the plainsmen, it had put an end to it. Nobody talked about this. Perhaps the plainsmen had fought, but the only distinguishable class here now was the army itself. Its paved barracks, glossy olive vehicles, cool stone and general spruceness were not popular. The soldiers and staff were accepted at present for they behaved equitably.

A single authority approved our journey in principle. "Anything else? No details please. Good. Good luck." At the Commissariat, it took us twenty minutes to learn what we could borrow, what we could buy, and what we'd have to get elsewhere. By midday, the available stores were in our lorry. There had been none of the red tape or the *"Mañana, mañana"* one might have expected in a British unit. They had been brusque, likeable and realist, with a single touch of swank. They said "——" in English sometimes, having been the only Latin-American force in the Korean war. A very nice junior officer, who'd served there, occasionally said "sheet" as well. "They're not bad, the soldiers," said Rafael. He seemed a little surprised.

. . . .

A different force, the Military Police, seemed rather arrogant, and cold to the people. They were fewer, and served as an instrument of politics, as was strictly logical. At night, someone struck a soldier and was hustled off at bayonet point by this force. The crowd watched over their man, silent but far from cowed and the troopers faced them in a circle with their weapons. When people were killed in Colombia under the dictatorship, it may have started like this.

The man was threatened, but not hurt; fined the next day and released, I think.

We needed more groceries from Bogotá, and funds were ready for me at the Ministry of Agriculture. I took the bus for economy, leaving about four in the morning.

By dawn, I realized that we were on a road. The driver had his head out of the window, looking at the edge, to keep us on it; for there was nothing solid below. Sodden bushes grew out from the cliff, outlined against a cold grey cloud. A boy came round to collect coins, which were offered at a shrine of the Virgin.

This stretch was cut through a yellow rock crumbling like cheese. The neat stone crosses along it warned us against the unavoidable instability of the roadway, as well as against casual driving. What could be done to keep the road on the face of the mountain was done. Someone pointed out how good it was, in the circumstances. It served to bring cattle from the plain, to fatten on the plateau. There was a common story about it:

"They used to take the herds up on foot. The cattle arrived thin."

One could imagine it. "They built the road and took them in lorries, as now. The drovers said the lorries would fall off. They did. Boulders kept dropping on them from high up."

We had breakfast at a market town, old and beautiful, shrouded in a cold mist. Farmers came to the square in matted *ruanas,* beaded with moisture, carrying potatoes or tropical fruit from fields a few miles apart. There was a beggar with sores on his legs, who asked for nothing, and was given nothing. We had more coffee and read about a beauty contest in the papers.

Beyond, the valley was wide, graced with pale willows and fresh streams between shadowy mountains. The road was capital, and a priest sat on my knees half the way as additional comfort.

The willows gave way to dark eucalyptus trees, and we rattled into Bogotá from the top of the pass, under a blackish pall. One saw it in a different light, after Villavicencio. The life seemed thin and sad, like the air.

I met cultivated people on my business, who deplored the uncouthness of the others: the word *"culto"* was continually on their lips. Well-off or not, they also disliked the signs of poverty or rusticity. They dressed well and worked hard in their offices from eight in the morning to five at night, speaking with elegance and wit, and eating where their sort of people gathered, or at home on the south side. They were decent and hoped to improve the nation for others to have similar advantages.

They might have been in London, New York or Rome. Many of them had, and wanted to return there. These cities were truly cultivated; the people didn't scowl at a man in a lounge suit; they'd give one service for a tip and wished their sons to be educated. The people there had never burst into the centre of town with rifles they shouldn't have had, ravaged the offices, turned over all the cars, and burned some of them with the occupants inside. That was how the war had started in 1948, continuing with the burning of churches and murder of priests in country districts.

It was seven years after. The floodlit church of Monserrate and the garish advertisement of a textile firm glowed by night on the black mountains. One was forbidden to have a rifle to shoot the advertisement out.

The cultivated class regretted the military rule, but considered it might be necessary for a time. The people were irrational, and the country would be politically unstable till they were more educated. Perhaps more social security, a workers' university, co-operatives or various new development projects were required: it all needed thought.

Only there was a doubt whether the people would appreciate this thought. It seemed they cared only for facts; and admired a canny person rather than a truly cultivated one.

An Englishman at a bullfight here sat next to a rough-looking man in a *ruana,* which the educated people in Bogotá didn't wear. The man offered him a swig from a grimy bottle of spirits, which my acquaintance refused. "And, you know, I thought he was going to knife me!" It was questionable who needed to respond to whom.

.   .   .   .

Sometimes the rain ceased. Men slung their coats over their shoulders, and even smiled cursorily; the city gleamed in a pure northern light. Yet I still felt home-sick, not for London.

I missed the heavy shadows, the weathered look of men and things, and the opaque, flatly objective way of speaking. In the plain, too, there was no vicarious shame. It was considered useful to know if a man stole, but it was his own business. He might even be maimed, or desperately poor, and not hide it, without anyone feeling embarrassed or disgusted.

.   .   .   .

At the Ministry of Agriculture I was given a form for a government grant. I was to collect the parasites of any animals killed in the Macarena. As the place had never been inhabited the animals would have their own particular parasites, if any; and if those attacked men or cattle we would have learnt what their original host was.

The Ministry had heavy responsibilities, and my business had gone through with little delay. The form was handed in at the Controlariat of Government Expenditure, amid the clatter and tinkle of typewriters. A young man had taken me here from the Ministry: "Please be my guide," I said, and he introduced me to some friends of his. The form was taken from a steel bureau and signed by eight agreeable executives. "How tall are you, Doctor?" "Where are you visiting?" "Is it to catch monkeys?"

I delivered my file, eight times heavier than at conception, and went single-handed to an office of disbursement for the cheque. Wistful government employees came each in turn to the glass plate with a metal slit in it, where the secretary told them to come again next week. The typewriters behind her, in the well of a huge building, roared like a sea of tin. The offices above were sealed and blank. The atmosphere was far more like Whitehall, yet even here something went wrong, for my cheque came out in the afternoon.

At the Army Commissariat office, where I needed permission to buy groceries cheap, a brusque colonel maintained his military bearing unperturbed by the officers' wives, or other relations, who called throughout the afternoon. All were of bewitching beauty and manner; each seeming, while she remained, more radiant than those who'd come before.

The stores were bought and dispatched by road; and I took the early morning plane to Villavicencio, not wishing to make that bus ride too often. We rose through swirling mist and rain, weaving over Monserrate.

.   .   .   .

Rafael, with Carlos helping him, had finished packing; I went to complete our arrangements. The Major whom I worried for things was not at headquarters. I studied the map of the plains and the bare whitewashed ante-room, and a young soldier tapped steadily at his typewriter through the afternoon. Burly landowners in faded shirts leaned across the windowsill for a casual word of business.

The Major came in from an inspection rather tired, and heard what I wanted: "Oh, yes, and one more problem—" "Is that all?" he said when I had finished. I thought so. "Well, come back tonight."

The tapirs joined me under the mango tree in the Institute, standing sideways with their noses bent up to the fruit in the branches. Each kept a dull brown eye fixed on me placidly. The mangoes were too high up, but they expected I'd put things right. At length, I bashed some down with a bamboo stem, and returned to the Major's office.

He came out smiling grimly. "Your plane leaves tomorrow morning at six-thirty. No more little problems, please. Goodbye."

Rafael and I discussed our needs: fish hooks, packing cases, cooking pots, a gas mantle, a machete, two small knives for skinning, the stuff from Bogotá, a lorry to take us to the airport at dawn, cigars, a gallon of petrol for lighting fires, candles, torch batteries, rum, matches, ammunition for the shot-gun . . .

The plane took timber, beer and fizzy lemonade to the pioneer village of San Juan de Arama, ten miles north of the Macarena. They planned to get a chapel built while the people were still thirsty and inaugurate it after.

The land was under flat tongues of forest and grass. Within the forest broad rivers, braided through gravel from the Cordillera, slipped off to the east, on their long journey under the sun to the Orinoco. I looked down, where our shadow travelled over the glossy dark treetops, frightening the macaws. A few of the trees were in blossom, or the mistletoe-like shrubs on their boughs

51

were: mostly white or violet-blue, a colour enticing to bees. The land was nearly empty, but in some of the tongues of the forest, sunk beneath the level of the tree crowns, lay patches of yellow earth within a stockade—with pigs inside, or a dog sleeping in the sun. In the hard deep shadows at the edge, a thatched hut would be concealed, where probably the farmer was sleeping amid the flies. Rafael told me the sonorous Indian names of the rivers one by one, and the more ordinary names of the few villages.

San Juan de Arama was in flat grassland like a meadow, enclosed in deep woods where the streams ran. We emerged blinking in the sun. The cargo was hauled out fast by a party of tough soldiers, who shouted cheerily "Hey Mister!" and "——" in English.

As soon as possible Rafael and I left the soldiers and went over to the village, where it was the siesta. The village was casual and reserved, made of dry palm stems and thatch, propped up with bamboo or timber frames. We drank cool and clear *guarapo*—raw sugar fermented in the dark—in the shade of a general store. A woman came in with a jug to top up the *guarapo,* which is kept fermenting; an old character with white whiskers sat on a bench. We discussed the Macarena in a leisurely way between rounds, for which Rafael paid more than his share. There was gold in the river there, though not much, and nobody knew which of the mountain streams it came down. The Jesuits had left a treasure there, whether of native gold or church funds they didn't know. It scarcely mattered.

Over the tree crowns of the far wood, the powder-blue hills lay in a column southwards under a blinding white sky. They had curved tree-covered tops like poodles' backs, separated by narrow vertical clefts. There was no cloud, but the hills boomed with thunder several times in the afternoon.

We expected to find another man here for the trip,

and called from door to door. "Someone who knows a bit . . ." said Rafael. I tried to get a toothbrush at the store: "They have them in the camp; they eat peccary there." In the village there were no guns. The store-keeper suggested Símon Sanchez-Gutierrez for the journey, and we went to his hut. He was lean and tall, with a face lined as though he had starved some time back, and a touch of sadness in his voice at times. The expedition was complete.

His house was such as a man would build with his machete, having the forest to make it from and furnish it. He played a record for us on a weathered gramophone, but the music was indistinct. "It's half broken," he said.

Outside, the army had planted and fenced saplings, and made holes for street lamps for a town of the future.

CHAPTER V

Escape

THE grass shone with heat and didn't move. Beneath it the baked surface of the plain was riddled with holes. They said the cool black chambers below would hold prairie-rats, bird-eating spiders, owls and boa constrictors. Sometimes a coarse lining of silk showed a big spider was inside.

As much as the animals, I felt the need for shade and went into the woods, slashing at the logs and hollow stems with my new machete. There were some black and lemon daddy-long-legs hidden in one: their colours implied they might be poisonous for a bird. I sliced into a wild pineapple and cut in half a crab-like spider which had been buried there. It grew too dark.

The grass outside had taken on a fresh yellow-green tint, broken by the feathery shadows of a few palms. The palms were graceful, but bristled with thin thorns. The pure two-note song of a black and yellow bird pierced the trees alongside. One never ate this bird.

Some village men were talking to the soldiers in camp, across the stockade. They were handsome, with level eyebrows, long narrow eyes, and steady features. They were discussing a game of football for the next day. As a point of courtesy I was invited to play with the soldiers; they said one of their team was ill. Having seen both teams and the pitch, about equally hard, I could well believe this and wondered where they'd buried him. Incidentally, the sentry on the gate challenged everyone with levelled rifle, though perhaps it was for discipline.

I hadn't time to play, for I was going to the Macarena as early as possible next morning. I made sure of this with the others.

The camp buildings were like the village, being out of the forest too; but stones for paving were brought up from a stream. The soldiers were quiet and grown-up for an army unit; orders were given and obeyed intelligently. At sunset there was a short, silent parade: they took the flag down and the sergeants came round a bamboo table for supper. Except for two from the Atlantic coast, the talk was as quiet as the candlelight. Their faces were leathery and expressionless, apart from a nice smile now and then: one couldn't read them.

These faces were descended from three continents and various peoples in each: Basque, Iberian, Moorish and Bantu, with highland and lowland Indians, strangers in one another's lands. The result was a deep reserve, and speech strictly to the point.

We had two bottles of *aguardiente* between us, of a delicate brand called by the local river, Ariari, which we drank fast and easily. I slept like a log in one of the sergeants' huts.

Rafael and Símon were roping our stores to three army mules. I tried to help them and did so eventually by going away. We said good-bye to the acting commander, an impenetrable sergeant-major, who'd been extraordinarily kind to us as though it were nothing. He was nursing a young deer, which put its hooves up and licked his nose. It was like seeing a rock smile.

With some soldiers to bring the mules back we went into the long grass drenched with dew. There was a narrow path all the way, fortunately, as the grass was matted and wiry.

Bursts of black seed-eating birds rose from in front, their scarlet shoulders flashing like sparks from a fire. We went through trees and a shallow stream; the grass stretched over to the next. It was alight in places, where birds of prey patrolled the smoke to seize anything which came out. An eagle passed us, with wings like scythe-blades.

Beyond, the plain was pierced by fresh shoots after a previous burning, for the cattle to eat later. I noticed the straight coppery stubble of a bird-eating spider, dead and upside down. It was hard and light, like the dried-up husk of a lemon.

The hills were dark behind a crest, as if the plain had been forced up at an angle without breaking. The crest was furrowed with clefts of streams. The blocks of mountains stood upright from their shadows in a fleece of tree crowns. Their colour like a deep sea was so youthful, and the hills so compact and square, they might have emerged from the horizon that morning.

We threaded our way across a broad meadow, grazed by heavy-shouldered Zebu cattle. The bulls had long purposeful horns hooked up and forwards; and when they cantered alongside us they made the earth thunder. We came to a low ranch, the only one in this corner of the plain; and rather slow-moving because the *patrón*, an army officer, was seldom there. We all said "Morning; how goes it?" and slumped in the shade to drink water and black coffee. We enjoyed a lazy and genial conversation about nothing. A black mongrel bitch which had accompanied us yapped at the chickens outside, and chased the cows.

Símon said, tentatively, "The bitch is mine for company in the woods." She was called *Esperanza*, meaning hope, which was the most one could do with her.

The sky was satiny, with flat cream-coloured clouds motionless on the ceiling. Beyond the ranch we were relieved to escape from it into the evergreen wood. The mules sniffed the foliage on each side and occasionally tore off a mouthful.

The forest sloped down beneath the surface of the

56

plain and a steady roar of water came through the leaves. There was light, and we were on the brink of a glacial green river, the Guëjar, borne from the springs and waterfalls within. It churned and fizzed vigorously through pools cut in the rock and over a carpet of boulders it had washed down. It was slightly bitter, and seemed to cure the dysentery I had in twenty-four hours.

We stumbled across the shallows, slithering on the insecure boulders and leaning against the surge. Esperanza struggled and whined and was borne towards a ledge, funnelled in by rocks, where the entire river dropped a yard. I thought she'd be killed and no one else seemed to care: animals die sooner or later in any event. However, she scrambled through the shallows and on to a low beach. She shook herself in the sun and barked furiously.

The far side was slow and muddy, overhung by a towering wall of forest, ragged on top, where the tree crowns spread under the sky. We went through a narrow slit at the bottom and crawled on to the bank.

.   .   .   .

A myriad of thin trees rose vertically from the floor, into rays of sunlight. We chopped carefully in a rough circle leaving a few poles to sling our hammocks on. Símon got some driftwood from the beach, doused it in petrol and dropped a match in; the fire started with a woof. I produced Pernod from the commissariat stores, which we drank with two parts of water in enormous mugs. Thus diluted it was like neat *aguardiente*; this caught the imagination of the soldiers. "Man . . . !" they said.

A huge butterfly, the blue trembling on its wings like electricity, flew about our clearing. Sometimes it vanished, being hidden in its folded wings on a certain twig in the centre. My possibly drunken swipes with a butterfly-net scared it away in the end.

A column of leaf-cutting ants marched across the log I was on, bearing circles cut from some strange translucent white leaf. I picked a worker up by the bit she was carrying: it was a piece of the polythene I had just unpacked to put specimens in. The first few feet of the roll were shot full of holes already, like a gruyère cheese. Anyway, this was to be our home.

The soldiers led their mules back over the ford; the fire smoked into our eyes; and Símon went to the beach with a ragged cigar in his mouth, and a few yards square of weighted net. He whirled this about his head and cast it into the shallows; picked it up and said "*Guaputas!*" He always expressed himself clearly. Rafael took machete and gun and moved into the woods. A pair of long-necked black ducks, their wings too small for their bodies, beat upstream round the bend. I went across, tied a rope to a tree, and bathed in the rapids hanging on to it. I was frightened of the fish anywhere else.

It was late afternoon, and the sunlight was golden. Many little green- and straw-coloured lizards crept from the shadows between boulders and perched on top, their throats pulsating. A star-like crack on a boulder, four or five inches wide, would abruptly vanish under one's shadow. This would have been a spider; the beach was alive with them, though arid and sterile.

The sun went down at six o'clock leaving a glow on the beach. Some quiet brown ibises crept under the trees, in file, cheeping secretly to each other. They kept ten feet from me as I followed them a little way down.

Símon had five ugly grey fish hung over the fire. We lit candles because the twilight doesn't enter the forest, and tried to start a petrol lamp, only the mantle was too big. Símon declared it wouldn't work. This was a silly defeatist attitude, and I took the thing in hand myself. It didn't work. One by one a quartet of frogs began a chorus on the far bank of the river, resounding like a gang of strong men sawing a hollow mahogany log. There was no other sound.

We ate, and drank coffee. As one washed one's plate, little fish gathered in a sudden boil of water, snatching the grains of rice from each other and the fibres off one's fork. Rafael stood quietly smoking, looking into the leaves: it was his luxury for the day. He was always silent at this time. Símon sat cross-legged on the ground, studying his long bony shins. "I'm thin," he stated gloomily. "Well you won't get any fatter here." It was a hungry place.

The conversation led on easily, its tone set by the two Colombians, factual, sometimes ironic, with an economy of words. "What came of the road?" This was to be built from San Martín to San Juan. "A colonel came and made a speech."

Their voices faded behind me. The forest changed constantly, as the trees one had passed closed in. The papery undersides of the leaves, pointed and smooth-edged, arched five or ten feet over one's head; above them were black spaces strung with a few thin branches, and the torch beam vanished. Sometimes ghostly white fragments of a trunk appeared at the end of the beam, a hundred feet up, like a floating marble pillar; or a black vine like a cable would coil down. The place was quite still.

There was a fallen tree with the earth clotted to the underside of its roots. A dull black whip-spider spanning ten inches was flattened against it, her feelers and claws folded at her side. Her legs were spiny, and the claws armed with spikes half an inch long; she was a lovely beast. One could play with her by vibrating a twig in the air. Her feelers unfolded in response to the vibrations and stretched out to locate them. She sidled round till she faced the vibrating twig, and braced her legs for a spring. Her claws opened and quivered. She was a living trap, sensitive to the wing-beats of insects. If they

59

settled there in the dark, the spikes would impale them.

The trees beyond had fallen, or were leaning against each other; and the ground was cluttered with dead wood and mushy new growth. Pale green vines, thin as bootlaces and nearly invisible, were threaded among the dead trees, and the sprigs dropped stinging ants down one's neck as one brushed by. Everything unpleasant in the forest was here. The patch was marked by a few brown tree-trunks with wing-like buttresses, many feet across.

An orange eye glowed at my feet: I could see nothing there and recoiled in case it was a snake. The eye still burned beneath the arums. It was a frog as big as my hand, blending with the dead leaves. It has been classified since and rests pickled in a corner of the Natural History Museum at South Kensington. It makes an interesting specimen because it has both suckers for climbing trees and webbing to swim. It had been comfortable among the arums and rotting wood, doing neither. It seems a sheer waste.

In camp Rafael and Símon hailed me, "What did you catch?" "A frog." "Plenty of those." "Well, what did you get?" "Cold." "I caught that too." We mixed and drank some milk powder—the sort of thing that really matters to have in exploring—and inspected our hammocks. They were compact military affairs borrowed from the army, with waterproof cover and mosquito-net in one piece. Rafael observed, that they seemed very good in all respects, except possibly to sleep in, which was the case.

I put my machete in the ground by the head of the hammock, leaned the gun on the bole of a young tree next to it, and snuggled down in my *ruana*. It was quite chilly.

From the hills over Villavicencio one had seen the whole plain, like a grey sea of grass, silent and with no lamp-light from the town to the horizon. There one had felt good. The unbroken light, between the grass and the white flat clouds on the sky, was like an ocean, one's own to swim under. Símon, who belonged to the plain, felt the same way about it, more deeply. When we got between the mountains he grumbled that there was no sun and no space and everything was wet; and he chopped a few trees down as protest.

Here was only the casual, though well-thought-out construction of the camp to look on after dark; the few spindly herbs on the ground, the arums growing on the log we used as a bench, and sprigs of leaves gleaming over the fire. Around the clearing it was all shadows, and above it pitch-black.

CHAPTER VI

Alarms

MANY spots of light gleamed in the tree crowns and filtered through the leaves below, speckling the floor with pale, broken images of the sun. They were about eight inches in diameter, from which one could have estimated the height of the trees, perhaps. I didn't think of it.

Rafael had already cut a long trail back from the river in search of a path he'd helped make a year or two earlier. It had been five feet wide, and if he could re-open it, we'd borrow the mules again to move in. His new trail was revealed by the gleaming cut ends of the saplings, a handsbreadth above ground. If one struck higher up the machete didn't bite. He worked over it again, slicing down easily, just in front of his toes.

Rafael called it clean or dirty forest. The dirty forest glistened with emerald leaves, sprouting from twisted trees and vines. They were mostly soft, but so interlaced one had to cut through scrupulously with a short knife. One smelt the rotting vegetation, some of it still upright. There were stinging ants, and vines with sharp spikes which kept them from slipping as they wove up.

The clean forest was spare, bony and durable. The trunks were extremely thin for their height, and straight or nearly so. Most were ash-grey, but a few burnt sienna, chocolate or blue-black, ascending like jets of water into the spray of leaves. We passed through a grove of trunks like cannon-barrels, the branches extending horizontally high above.

Beyond, a thin veil of leaves darkened the air. A dozen little birds moved in a silent cluster to the bank of a stream, where the light petered out totally. It became still: the leaves seemed suspended in the air. They were stiff, like bottle-green spearheads, but cool and gentle to touch. The long stems and stalks were delicately balanced, crossing each other.

We heard a noise in the vault, and crept among the lower trees to a clear place. Three burly red monkeys ambled about the almost bald boughs of an old giant in the sunlight. They barked and groaned, and one of them grasped a branch with both hands and shook it frantically. Several twigs and a few heavy nuts crashed through; we backed away. In this type of wood, the nuts of some trees grow heavy and hard as bowls. The monkeys were howlers, demonstrating against us.

At the end of the path lay a hot pool of light where a tree had fallen recently. Its crown, buried in clinging plants, barred our way. We scrambled ten or twenty feet among the branches, to search for landmarks. Only the spreading crowns of the highest trees could be seen over the lip of the clearing: five or six of them, the furthest some seventy yards off. A couple of birds made a noise like an oboe somewhere in the forest behind. We climbed down, and I wiped my face on my shirt sleeve. Rafael's face was like mahogany, but he dabbed at it with a red handkerchief. He was happy, so far as a very stoical man can show it, peering into the wood with satisfaction, and a certain benignity. As we stood and smoked, an attenuated dragonfly, five inches long with slender gold-tipped wings, fluttered slowly across the path. We went back to camp, where Símon had made coffee.

Rafael told me the forest was like this everywhere he'd been; for instance in Vaupés where he had worked as a rubber collector. Slavery and terrorism had been usual on the estates before his time—under the Peruvians, he said. (Things were well organized now, by an American firm.) Beyond the path, lying south-east, the forest continued tree after tree, except for rivers, a ninth of the way down the world across flood plains and low hills.

We had a bag of crude brown sugar in bricks; I got one and nibbled it, noticing that the bag was covered in stupefied black bees, swollen with the sugar they had drunk, and docile. They either couldn't sting or didn't want to. They were nice clean animals, much preferable to flies. The shimmering blue butterfly of the previous day appeared again briefly; we didn't molest it.

We ate a tin of salmon and drank pints of black coffee, making plans. I had maps given me by the Shell Company of Colombia, marking tributaries of the river. We were at the top of a bend and streams flowed in both directions from the highest ground south of us. Rafael chose to continue his path towards one of the brooks marked, on which the earlier expedition had made house; and I to look for a different one flowing west, up-stream. The bends of the river showed it would be deep in the mountains.

Various butterflies floated through in ones and twos; monkeys and strange birds emerged and disappeared overhead. Occasionally, a long way off, some unseen animal would squeak, bark, whistle or groan as it went by; and clear prints showed on the sand outside. Both of us were inclined to enter as far as we could, and stay there looking—for nothing in particular.

The whole forest was open if one went carefully; but one searched as if the shadows held a bodiless odour, which was attractive. In Rafael the feeling lay deep, I believe.

In Símon it wasn't there at all. He said: "There are plenty of animals here. Let's stay and get some women." I hadn't thought of this but said, through shyness, innocence or conceit, that I had to go back to England;

64

when I left there'd be crying, and it wouldn't be convenient. Anyway I was engaged and very faithful.

"I know several women in San Juan . . ." Símon went on.

Unfortunately we hadn't enough food or spare money. He was joking anyway.

It was untidy upriver. Dirty forest hung over the water, its branches dragging, and in places falling in. Dead bamboos, thirty or forty feet long, flopped head down in the shallows, tied to their stumps by a few fibres; and sun-bleached logs lay stuck on their roots above the rapids. The river had heaped boulders and jetsam near the bank, and undercut the earth and tree roots, so they tottered as one scrambled over them. The tips of waterlogged branches came through the surface, with straws and floating weeds wrapped round them from upstream.

A sluggish brook crept into the river from inside the forest, leaving a bed of mud at its mouth, which was apparently bridged by a fresh and firm tree trunk. That was an illusion: termites had eaten away every particle of wood inside, leaving the shell of bark complete. I moved amphibiously.

While wading I wanted a stick, to prod for sting-rays, and because the footing was uncertain. The sticks on land were termite-eaten, but I saw one semi-waterlogged on the bottom, slanting towards the surface, and bent to pick it up. This was an illusion too; before grasping, I saw that it was an electric eel.

I edged into the bank to avoid spreading vibrations in the water. I couldn't see in while standing straight, but bent over and looked through my shadow. The eel was subtly edging in with me. It was in calm water, and a ripple passed along its fin. I floundered to the bank and leapt out.

The river sparkled tranquilly, reflecting the creepers over the opposite bank. It was quite safe really; I never saw another electric eel in this water. Many other places are far more risky, but one is accustomed to them. Later, Rafael said "The eels aren't dangerous in themselves. The trouble is if they knock one unconscious one drowns." It's this sort of accident that gives the place a bad name.

I sat on a rock and smoked, not for pleasure, but to keep the midges away. These insects must be got over with, so far as that is possible, to save tedium. They were square-built, black flies with powerful thoraxes and big heads, approximately a tenth of an inch long. They bit from dawn to dusk, and we lived in a thin but pervasive cloud of them. They were wherever the river could be heard; they breed in fast water. Hovering in clear sunlight or in the broken shade of the forest, they were invisible, so it seemed as if the air stung. They flew silently, alighted without one's feeling it, and were off again as obvious as ghosts. The bite was itchy for twenty minutes, but the effect cumulative. After walking on the beach or in the river, where they were most numerous, one was swollen, scratching and cross for an hour. In the forest, however, it was sufficient to keep moving.

They flew up one's trouser legs, but not down one's collar. They most frequently bit out of sight, under the chin, on the back of the neck or the lower side of a forearm; but if seen they vanished, wafted off in the air current preceding the slap. It still mystifies me what they ate as a rule; for there seemed to be a greater amount of these little black flies than of blood to go round among them. Were I selling the Macarena, I should point out there were very few mosquitoes there.

The river flowed through a sheer cleft under the peak of a green mountain, which it seemed to have sliced in half. On the far side rose the ledge of grass we'd seen from the plain, behind a spreading forest like ivy. A great white vulture floated almost motionless against the mountain, and the water poured out below, green, clear and fluted by the lines of current.

The previous wet seasons, a desert of boulders, mud and sand had been washed up in the crook of the river. I had thought to cross and look back at our mountains from the outside, but hadn't learned where to trust the water, and trotted along the beach to keep ahead of the midges. There were footprints ahead of me.

They had told me to watch out, in case rebels from the '48 war were still hiding there. I watched out: a blank wall of green encircled the beach.

On my return, Símon said: "Yes, we found footprints too. People from the ranch and from San Juan come here to shoot and fish; that's all." Rather a let-down. They left to hunt, taking both guns. The air was heavy and smelled sweet; the fire smoking palely, and the black bees hummed on the sugar bag. I found a tick on my knee, singed its abdomen with a cigarette end, and removed it.

A muted clucking aroused me before dusk. A troop of slender, chestnut turkeys tiptoed through the leaves behind the clearing. They were at ease, and occasionally stabbed down for a grub. I thought: dinner, breakfast, lunch, dinner, breakfast, lunch—they'd be going bad by then—dinner . . .? One by one they trod delicately into the gloom. Rafael and Símon came after dark with a coati, inedible, but a specimen. They were philosophical over the wasted opportunity. Come to that, they hadn't seen me hit anything. I wasn't, for the same reason. We opened a can of tunny-fish and munched it.

We looked over our stores. "No women," commented Símon to himself. "After a single night—" Rafael pointed out. "A night single, man!" "Shameless."

The coati lay gleaming in the firelight, chestnut brown. It looked as a tree-going fox would, but sleeker and heavier built, with sharp curved claws and a wavy banded tail.

"It was in a tree."

Needing to preserve its parasites, I boiled a powder, paraformaldehyde, in a cooking pot. We recovered in a few minutes, and they observed, objectively: "The vapour is savage."

Símon puffed a cigar and watched me sealing my polythene tube, from a safe distance, as he admitted. The plastic bubbled round my heated knife blade and came away in a hot glutinous mass.

"Let's see."

I gave him some and burned a couple of holes in my trousers. . . . "Like that?" He'd sealed his perfectly with the cigar.

The parasites were preserved, sealed, labelled and afterwards lost. A skin was left of the coati.

. . . .

Rafael and I went hunting some more, separately. The night was dark and gusty. The water on our side seeped over a rock bed, from one black pool to the next between the forest wall and a wooded island. It was like following a river in a cave. Overhead, the leaves hissed against each other. A round orange eye, like a topaz, glimmered beyond my torch beam. It slid smoothly and steadily to the right as if on wheels, and disappeared. Only a quiet pool was there, with a carved tongue of rock lapping into it.

A similar eye appeared upstream over the rapids, as if fixed among the boulders. I loaded with heavy shot, to break through the skull, and fired directly at the eye. It went out. Then it reappeared further back, moving into a bay where it sank. The bay was shallow, with a sandy bottom, and a motionless six-foot alligator lay with its snout near the waterline. It didn't appear to be hurt; and there was no blood in the water. I poked the tail with a machete, and it drew forward a bit. The second poke, it suddenly rushed off into the dark water, spreading waves on to the beach.

Rafael had killed a little snake on the path. It was limp and smooth, mottled brown and grey, its head crushed by the machete blade. It had been quite harmless, but I didn't tell him so. I was no longer sure of such things here. "Fierce," he said. "Pity it had to be spoilt." It was hung on a vine, to preserve in the morning.

CHAPTER VII

Exploration

IT was Christmas Eve, and I had been woken by a bird singing in the cadence of a peal of bells. The note was silvery and very soft, wobbling between scales, or repeating bits doubtfully. We heard it once more three or four weeks later: the bird was never seen.

I had thrown rocks in the river, to frighten any dangerous fish away, and swum. Rafael said it was unnecessary there, and the noise wouldn't frighten the fish anyway. The sting-rays were in mud or sand, where they could hide; the *caribes* way downstream in warm water, and the electric eel in still places only. It's built to glide in a slow stream and make little vibration there, as it closes in.

We had gone over our plans again: it didn't seem necessary for Rafael to continue his path while I was looking for the stream to the west. "But it may be more convenient," he had said, "in case you don't find it." He was working steadily inland, scarcely seeming to raise the machete between strokes. "Do you know this?" He pointed at a leaf; I didn't know it. He'd sliced through the twig: hundreds of ants came scampering out, and poured over the stem.

"One doesn't have to touch 'em," he observed. ". . . I cut through a tree of this, for interest, and it's always hollow all the way through, with ants inside. I think the hole is natural, and not made by the ants, because it's very regular." He paused.

"And below them you see the ground bare, but I don't know the reason."

He walked to the end, myself helping to clean the path a little behind him, and came back treading softly, as if hunting. It is usually the case with travellers that they learn nothing for themselves, but are shown it.

.   .   .   .

The sun was already falling when I got to the mountain upstream, whose great shadow lay over the beach. Several pieces had dropped from the peak into the river, and others lay where it came out of the sand. Through these rocks one could scramble under the cloak of forest. It was nearly dark inside, because the light was lost among the higher leaves as in a venetian blind. I found a flat place about twenty feet up; took some dry wood there from the beach, and slung my hammock.

The river and the heavy rocks it cut through were obscure, swishing and humming in a slate-coloured light. When I turned the torch on, the eye of a narrow-headed bird glowed from the rock in mid-stream. It faced me for a few seconds, and took off in silence; its slight shape passed across the sky.

I got a can full of water, splashed petrol on the wood, and threw lighted matches in so carefully that the petrol had nearly vaporized before it caught. Nasty smell of singed hair, but no damage. My coffee was made eventually, and fell into the fire with a derisory hiss. It began raining.

A pale form of smoke hung over the firewood when the rain had finished. I crawled out in a shower of rain-drops from the saplings holding my hammock, and revived the fire, or else it revived me. I made plenty of coffee and ate half a brick of sugar with some tinned fish.

The raindrops sparkled by torchlight on the leaves around and still trickled down the white bark. Small hairy moths swarmed over a shirt I had changed, sucking it for salt or vitamins, and a big white one sat against a tree stem, shivering with its wings.

I got in the hammock, with the knife and gun, and stuck the machete alongside. More rain came through the trees on to the cover and plopped to the ground. My cigarettes were still dry, and strong enough to smoke in the dark, swinging myself by the machete handle. I dreamed of what there might be in the hills—giant sloths, little pterodactyls, or maybe an unknown snake. There'd been a snake in Paraguay ages ago, which left a poison fang there, big as a meat hook. This was a good place for anything to hide.

With my brain idling this way, I imagined a clear, pebbly stream about two feet deep. There was a grey, shelly creature like an insect darting along the bottom; its movements were very jerky and abrupt for anything in water. It was uncertain whether I caught it or not, but I hoped so. It seemed to be a trilobite; and these animals were extinct before there were crabs in the sea. Símon had been helping me catch the trilobite, but went off. There was a dark hole in the undergrowth where several black and yellow snakes had clustered together, wriggling. Their crisp lemon bands were distinct and the rest hardly visible. They seemed small, active and round-bodied. I wondered if this were foresight, the snakes being unknown to me. They didn't seem very important, and the daydream went on, but I forgot everything else as soon as it happened. No blue-winged butterfly had appeared—"immense and luminous as an archangel, which is the last vision of those who die of fevers here." (J. E. Rivera: *La Vorágine.*)

At this time, greenish-white gnats flew about, confined to the darkness. I had to sleep with the net shut and the machete outside, but it didn't matter at all.

. . . .

72

A turkey's neck appeared against the hot sand at the bottom among the vines, and I shot it. The bird was completely dead and difficult to find. It lay under its wings in a dry creek, like a pool of shadow. The feathers on the head were curly, and turned forwards, over a red bill. I cleaned it, and enclosed it in the hammock, to prevent the ants. It would feed us two or three times; a reasonable kill for Christmas Day, if we were to have meat.

It seemed exceptionally quiet, for the turkey had been making a low resonance which I had not noticed till it was stopped. The trees on this slope were straight and thin, as if the mountain hung from them. A few straight vine-roots like plumb-lines came down among them, connecting the light with the earth. Occasionally a horny leaf dropped through the shade, making me jump.

The trees ended leaning over a dark cliff where the trunks were a bit spindly. Our future hunting ground lay below: a row of steep green hills like dogs' teeth, the river cutting into them. A mile on lay smoother hills, turquoise under the haze, which we never reached.

I went into a nearly dead ravine, where the sun-spots drifted over sterile grey sand. Water from the wall splashed into the sand, making a rivulet where trees grew. It was a sad-looking place.

A path led through, that I was maybe the first human to follow. It was clear for any creature less than a yard high and fairly thin. They had taken it along a rock face, above the water, where I should not have gone otherwise.

Slender trees and creepers brushed the mountain-side, and shafts of light came through them. When Rafael and Símon got here, they admired the place for its beauty.

The path opened on to a broad slope where the animals would have gone freely, and here it broke into narrow passageways, through heavy vines. A snake would have tripped in them. The thick ones parted under a machete, and their stumps sweated orange gum. It was the green stringy ones that gave the entertainment, especially those with sharp-toothed ridges or spines.

Here was the stream, bitter as gin, among cream-coloured rocks it had stained magenta on top. A tortoise lay on the bank. I patted its box and it shut up with a hiss of musty air from the lungs. So it was still alive. We'd come here.

The turkey was still in my hammock, and I took it back for a sort of Christmas dinner. We drank Pernod in moderation, and they talked of incidents in the war.

"I don't understand how men can do things like that. . . ."

Símon spaced the logs out in the fire so that they'd smoulder all night.

.   .   .   .

Rafael had been unable to reopen the old path, because there was no trace of it. He cut a long way in, but the stream, to which the old path had led, wasn't visible either. "It must still be there, but it isn't." The next morning before breakfast, he cut through the very dirty forest upriver, to the beach below the mountain.

I untied a small alligator, my only capture, which had been on a leash in the pool below camp. It had become quiescent, and after thrashing momentarily when gripped, it went dead. It stayed there several minutes after release, then wiggled away like an enormous tadpole.

We harnessed ourselves with the sacks of provisions. Rafael showed how to tie loops of rope at the sides for the shoulders, and adjusted his load. "What do you carry?" asked Símon. "Six stone." "*Guaputas.* Two for me." "Oh. Help me on with it, man." "Damn heavy," said Símon. "No———." They moved off, Símon talking profusely. I found I could work harder than either of them, but only carry half as much.

It was hot. The path wound among the thicker patches to a little clearing where we rested and smoked. Beyond was a spit of sand overhung by leathery boughs, where one could walk easily. Then again through the woods, ducking under loops of vine and bent trees. There was a kind of clawed grass where the light entered, of which the fruiting heads came off in great quantities, clinging to one's trousers and dragging behind, while the seeds worked in and scratched one's leg. If one pulled this stuff off, and didn't keep a careful eye on it, it would hop on again.

This grass was a sign that animals came through here; and on the sand below the camping place, we found the broad prints of a jaguar, which confirmed that impression.

After two or three journeys we slung our hammocks and went to collect bits of driftwood from the beach. Símon started the fire and tied a green pole over it to hang the cooking pots. The real vines were little use for lashing, but the thin roots that came down from plants in the tree crowns were very strong and supple. One sliced them off as high as possible, and the cut end rose up again, hanging a little out of reach when one wanted it next.

We ate the rest of the turkey, roasted at my suggestion. The meat was simply left on spits leaning near the fire, till nicely done. It was terrible. Boiled, one couldn't have a tastier bird.

We spent a long time drinking coffee and talking. ". . . They're all dying for some sergeant," said Símon, a trifle mordantly, of the girls in San Juan de Arama. "They're the same everywhere," said Rafael. Also, they didn't wish to stay in the plain.

Símon went to the river, as watchful and still as a heron, admiring the view chiefly as it was too deep for his throwing net. Esperanza raced along the waterline, barking and frightening the butterflies, which whirled in the slight breeze like handfuls of big confetti. They tested the mud at several points and regathered, one after the other, on some particular patch. They jostled, flapping and pushing each other's wings at first.

They became still. The wings were half closed, mostly pearl-white, apricot or lemon tints, and a few some vivid colour against black. The tongues were looped into the mud and crossed each other. They opened their wings slowly when there was room, and snapped them shut again.

Sometimes a butterfly crossed from one little cluster to another; there was no other disturbance, and none ever settled long on the empty expanses of mud which were equally damp. They'd be picked up by their wings sooner than quit, and return straight to it, they were so intent.

If the whole cluster was driven off, they always re-settled at the same place, or on the same slime if it were shifted. I couldn't tell what the attraction was.

Símon saw a huge ray, and ran to cut and sharpen a pole. It took him ten strokes of the machete, and when he went to spear it, it was gone. "Pity," I said. "Doesn't matter. It was very big." He spread his arms out. "There wasn't much chance."

We listened for shots all through the afternoon, as Rafael was hunting somewhere. He reappeared quietly at dusk. "Nothing but a few monkeys, and I don't like to kill monkeys." "The meat's no good," said Símon, "though one can eat spider monkey." "I have, but it's still not good to kill these animals." I said I might have to, for their parasites, if there were no others.

"Yes. It's better to take certain other kinds. These

76

are too human." It is true enough, seeing that one can catch yellow fever from them.

We heated a tin of beef, and chose the potatoes to eat with it. Not many were left, and these were half rotten. We'd have to go to San Juan for some more.

The stars came out, as it was the dry season; we drank coffee and smoked on the beach, immediately under the forest. I buried my legs and one arm in the sand, which was still warm. It kept them from the midges, and seemed to soothe the old bites. The sky appeared to glow among the overhanging leaves, whose blackness served to reveal the deep colour.

Occasionally one of us crept off to see if any animal had come to drink further down the beach. This was possible, as we were concealed by the mountain. Its eyes would have shown in the torch beam swept round.

One kept feeling there was some movement beyond the beam; but it was only shadows. "The torch is very good," said the Colombians, "but perhaps more useful to leave behind." One hunted by lying very still on a beach, waiting.

"Being eaten by the midges?"

"That is the inconvenience," Rafael observed. "But with the light and movement the animals are frightened."

"They are very timid when they come to drink, because the jaguar hunts them then."

But I'd looked for prints and there weren't any. They agreed one couldn't be sure after a single trial. "This thing is new to us. But after hunting the other way, that seems best." Perhaps the animals would come on a darker night.

CHAPTER VIII

Hunting Ground

A SLIGHT mist spread over the sky next day, and the specks of light in the wood were gentler. This meant rain, though we never saw it coming. It came suddenly after dark, falling straight and hard on the forest, as if from a great height. In a few minutes the first drips plopped to the ground, and in quarter of an hour the higher tree stems were wrapped in smooth sheets of water. They flowed on another fifteen minutes, after the rain stopped. It was convenient weather, if the water didn't enter one's hammock at night.

Esperanza began to whine occasionally. "She has worms," said Símon. He meant warble-fly maggots in the flesh of the back, but I didn't understand this. At the same time, she gathered ticks. It made her ill company, for she spread them abroad by rubbing herself; Símon and I drove her away when she came too near. Rafael didn't, as he was less inclined to fuss.

That we caught few parasites ourselves was due to having no fur. We could easily keep our skins dry and clean, and burn the occasional tick off with a cigarette end. We also had medicines, tobacco, mosquito nets and insect-repellent to save ourselves from the least annoyance.

From her condition, Símon should never have brought the bitch into the forest; yet it didn't seem or feel at all harmful here.

Cool clumps of arum grew on the mountain, in which

one could lie back as a rest from hunting. Sometimes an indigo butterfly would flit over the dead leaves, which the mild light at this time flecked with golden tints; or a bronze hummingbird whizzed overhead. There was nothing destructive, except a little spider, coloured like a wasp, with long curved spikes, which had put its web between two arums.

I went several times over the mountain, though there was nothing to eat there, on the excuse of finding an easier way to the stream.

The slope was furrowed in places, as if a monster had dug ditches in it, which had become rounded by now with gaunt grey trees inside and spiky wild pineapples along the edge. The bottoms were full of dry leaves that rustled loudly when one crossed them, and would have frightened the game off.

The ravine at the far end was formed like these furrows, and no wider, but extremely deep. It bent round and forked under the forest, separating three enormous pegs from the rest of the mountain. The floor sloped inwards, opening from the air some seventy yards above the river. The only way beyond was the animals' path I'd seen already.

The water must have flowed round the peak at some time, and along the brink of the ravine. Occasionally macaws flew there, filling the space with their noise: "Yainh, Yainh, Yainh."

The land had been cut away from that height, leaving the mountain, and this ghost of a torrent two-thirds of the way down, printed vertically into the rock. It was overgrown, and dark inside, so one couldn't easily make it out.

The river must have rasped further into the country every wet season, like a saw, and the dust rumbled along it. The boulders on the beach, weighing about a ton, rested casually on each other and rolled when I walked over them.

Bare land was strewn each side of the river, with young growth taking over quickly. Stiff shoots of grass, swarming with lizards, poked through the sand; tangled forest came up over the mud.

Certain trees, growing as high up as our camp, stood two or three feet off the ground on their roots, as though on tiptoe to escape the excess of water; but more likely to feed in it. It had gone down; and the dead logs on the beach were as hard and pale as weathered bones. Spiders lived in the cracks.

One couldn't recognize the domain of the river; I was vaguely aware of it. For one thing the midges grew as larvae hanging to the rocks in mid-current. In a sense they lived on the fast eating-away of the land; and formed a perceptible dark haze in hollows skirting the wood.

The overgrown riverside smelt faintly, of trees choked while green, or enriched soil.

Thin black ribbons appeared at its edge, stretching far among the shaded pebbles. A few similar ribbons passed through the growth. They were stationary, but shimmered, changing their position at times; while the shining ants they were made of raced like sand in a steady wind till they bit into something. It was easy to tell if anyone stepped in them, by his stamping and undressing suddenly; but they never ran out from their paths and seldom caught anything. They'd have fed mostly on dead meat, left from the alterations of the river and the hunting along it.

The second day, Rafael was showing me an insect that crawled backwards through the dead leaves and resembled them exactly. "Very curious," he said. "They are common," said Símon. He was listening to something else. "Give me the gun a moment." He aimed upwards, where I could see nothing. The turkey fell directly from its branches, nearly into the cooking pot.

In the evening he'd shown me where an electric eel

was hunting. I could see only stony water; but there was a white flash from the belly of a stunned fish. It was surely too big for the eel; in a moment it floated down and out of sight, possibly recovering. The fish were crowded in the shrunken river.

Back in the mountain furrows and the ravines, where the water had left its mark and there was no further change, the leaves seemed dusty and nothing ever stirred them.

.   .   .   .

I'd left a pair of cellular nylon pants in camp, and when I picked them up termites crawled over my hand. They covered the material. It gave me the creeps slightly, but it was interesting to watch them chew the stuff, already somewhat more cellular. I brushed them off. Rafael said they'd eat anything. "They have no dignity," said Símon. Yet the living trees round us were not touched, nor the bark of dead trunks, which I'd frequently sat on expecting solid wood inside.

There was a harsh deep noise during the rain; and I don't think it was thunder. A jaguar left new prints on the sand below us the next two mornings. Rafael said it would probably have disliked our smell.

CHAPTER IX

Interval

WE heard a sound like the wind blowing through wires. It seemed to hang over the mountain, rising and falling vaguely, and then it stopped. There was no answer.

Símon gave me coffee. "Howlers," he said softly when they had finished. "Don Rafael's out looking for them." Rafael came back and we finished the bird for breakfast. He'd seen them go on to a forested cliff where one couldn't follow.

Símon said they were dangerous: "They can kill a jaguar by throwing big nuts down." Then it would not kill them when they had to descend. "That's what people say," he added. "It might even be true." We could scarcely tell that it wasn't.

We saw these monkeys only among the highest spots of light, moving deliberately. If they seemed to think, or to communicate, it wasn't for long. They'd suddenly drop themselves downhill, through the trees, and their fingers left the boughs trembling. They must have been very strong for their size. Símon said they'd come down to eat limestone; hence their feud with the jaguar, if it was true.

The jaguar was no more to us than prints, and a smell of carrion in some bushes near the river. We might feel safer with it about because it would prevent others hunting here. Only we'd never seen it, or know if it was walking round us in the rain at night.

Símon asked me what I wanted to do, so he could help. We'd been searching the forest for ten days with no stated object; I think he was a little dissatisfied.

There was enough to do. One could spend twenty minutes any time adapting the army hammock for sleep, or seeking a flat stone on which to grind one's knife. Rafael had gone cutting a path up the mountain: later we would kill enough food to stay here, by using the silence of these paths.

"I'd like to see the animals." "I can get them for you." "Good, but to see them in the woods . . ." "Well, you should wear shoes like mine and go very carefully." He wore moccasins. "You make a noise and they are frightened." This was still true. One had to learn a taste for silence, to practise it enough.

I was squatting over a brilliant feather with tufts of down where a scuffle had taken place among the dead leaves. There were seldom remains of any creature in the forest, still less of their meeting. It had been a bird and something else. With a few light steps, the legs of peccaries came into sight under the screen of floor plants. They trotted some paces more and stopped, snorting quietly all round me. They were ten or twelve, compact grey animals with big triangular heads. Standing up with a machete, and glaring distrustfully at them, I was now a disturbing and bizarre spectacle. They stepped nearer and turned their heads to examine it. I struck at a log several times, to show ferocity, and they were gone.

Perhaps the casual movements of a creature minding its own business would not have disturbed the peccaries, but it had been untactful to get up and stare at them. One is never tactful and frightened. Anyway, I could see the animals if they came to look at me. They had appeared flat and shadowy and made little sound.

About now the air rose from patches of sun, and would set a palm leaflet shivering and ticking steadily against its neighbour. It was near midday; a few solitary wasps worked over the forest, while the light and perhaps the disturbance of the air favoured them against spiders. They moved in short hops, flicking their wings, while their bodies quivered like the heat. Sometimes there was a broken buzz when a dark wasp fanned the air backwards and strained on the leg of a paralysed tarantula. There'd be a hole made for it somewhere, and the wasp would take her bearings every three or four yards finding her way. It was out of time. For an hour or two, rather like midnight, this was the sole movement or noise; the wasp never stopped. The light was vertical; and the sky beyond the leaves appeared white-hot, without change.

A tree stood near a dry creek, with stubby thorns covering the trunk. It cast a heavy shade, with vines hanging round it. A few berries, half-pods, and papery dead leaves were stuck to the trunk on the thorns. Some of them were high out of reach; and no people lived here anyway. They made no pattern; there was no trace of whatever put them there. In the shade one scarcely noticed them.

We came across two or three trees treated this way, with the pieces stuck accurately through their centres. One could imagine a bird perching on the thorns, pushing a berry on with its bill, and getting something else; but the sense of it would be only for that kind of bird.

Perhaps all my notions of what the animals knew or wanted were a fantasy. They might drink for salt, eat for medicine, hunt for fear or sing to wake themselves; I'd guess wrong in each case. There would always be a difference between my reason and theirs; and it would seldom be obvious. The plain things we sensed, living in the same forest, might be entirely different. There was life here, but it would tell me no more than the howling of the monkeys.

Símon had fished from the beach all morning, under his hat, without catching anything. "There are fish, though?" "They are timid. They don't bite because the current makes them nervous." This was reasonable; and his tackle seen in the clear water could have frightened a crocodile. "Ah, misery!" he said, leaning back against a tree-trunk. His eyes shone brilliantly in the light from the river, where the butterflies were clustered on their mud; and he knocked the ash off his cigar.

Rafael waded from the far bank, resting a hand on his machete handle to keep the blade level over the water. The current eddied past him as round a rock. "Long walk." "I made a path to the top."

He told us everything he'd seen: the heart-breaking view from the top, of lands we'd never get to; a beach on the other side, with peccaries and their young ones drinking and playing; a black turkey, and the heavy forest to the west. It seemed we'd been here long enough.

.   .   .   .

A cicada sounded like a can of nails in my ear-drum, shaken slowly, faster, and stopping abruptly.

Símon was finishing a table of palm and bamboo, without nails. "Good sleep?" . . . "One can do nothing in the afternoon." It was a fair line of blarney, but I didn't feel ashamed anyway. It could make very little difference here what I did.

"Why will the midges bite gringo and not Colombian?" "For the fatness," he answered. They wouldn't lose the taste; I could sit and accustom myself to them if I chose.

With the sun falling, a few birds usually began to cry in the forest. They were louder this time, and a grey hawk flapped slowly over the top to an old tree by the beach. The birds came in from the mountain and far along the river, beating round the tree and screaming: they didn't worry the hawk. They seemed to be scaring themselves with it, and worked into a screaming frenzy as they broke off. Their noise spread into the dusk,

85

dying away, while the hawk glided to the next tree and settled itself.

It was a little chilly on the beach, and I took some dead wood in for the fire. Símon said there was no point as he had nothing to cook, but we found a few more tins.

Rafael came from hunting after dark, and we considered moving on. He said there were turkeys over there, and we could scarcely kill less than we had. "In the high mountains they go in flocks. . , ." It was too bad; here we'd be hunting without pause, and kill meat on any occasion we found it.

The fish were shy, and the alligators not the edible kind: we had little choice.

I mentioned the tortoise by the stream, if it was still there: "They're disgusting," said Rafael. "They were eating carrion back on the old path; also here where you threw the tripes of the turkey. Personally I shan't eat such animals. Very interesting because I never knew it before."

We'd get the potatoes from San Juan after cutting a path round the mountains, and then we'd go.

A frog yarped on the far side for an hour or two, as the fire died down. It was near the end of the change, from noon to dead of night, and nearly all movement came to a stop again. The spiders waited on their twigs.

CHAPTER X

Inland

THE trip to San Juan was not a success. We had to get cassava instead of potatoes; I bought too few cigarettes and some very bad cigars; there was no mantle to fit our lamp; the turkey I brought in for the N.C.O.s at the garrison scarcely went round and was rather tough anyway.

Símon had killed a tapir two nights before, and took half the meat home to his wife, so I imagined he did better. I had no story to tell the sergeants over supper; the party was dull. The lieutenant in charge had just broken his thigh, as one would expect, playing football against the village. He seemed rather subdued. I got some *aguardiente* to cheer us both up; but next morning, as he observed, he felt even worse. With the usual courtesies on every side, we left.

A rider came over the grass to us, and passed the time of day with Símon. . . .

"By the way, your enemy's in the district again, and has a gun." "That's all right; there are three of us and we're armed." It was flattering to be counted in, of course.

The horseman left; we came near the ranch. I asked if he had a quarrel. "No." "Then, about your enemy?" "Oh, someone." We never saw him.

We arrived at noon, the river glaring like steel, and wreathed in midges. Only crossing it this time we came back into our own world as though from a play, forgetting everything behind. There was no scenery here. It wasn't entirely agreeable, as my feet swelled amazingly on the boulders going back upstream.

Rafael had stayed behind and had no trouble. I tightened the hammock and put my feet up to let the blood drain from them. Lines of ants crossed the clearing for crumbs of meat. We'd killed rather too much just lately; the rest had been hung up to smoke and dry over a fire on the beach. Beyond the clearing were three tortoises, as Rafael had said, pulling at some offal we'd thrown away.

"They must be canny, to crawl so slowly and arrive ahead of the vultures."

Símon put up his own hammock in place of the army one, and would have slept well. It rained heavily, which stopped the curing of our meat.

The ground steamed and smelt sharp in the morning while drying off. I searched again east of the mountain for an easy way to the stream; we had tried twice already.

The trees and the land alike were gouged out into shadowy buttresses and empty creeks that wound under the dead trunks. I had killed a squirrel here, not seeing it clearly, and examined it for parasites without finding any. My path had been improved rather, second time round, but still led back to the same vaguely recognizable place.

Beyond, the ground was flat and almost empty, with dark fallen trees like great wigwams where an animal might lurk. It could have been a swamp at times. A bell-like alarm came through the leaves, though I was in stockinged feet.

Somewhere about, two ground-turkeys had been shot, tiptoeing under a palm frond and stabbing swiftly for grubs. The others had grunted and squealed like hogs as they fled, which might have confused an enemy. It was quiet today. A leaf-like spider dropped out of its web ahead of me, as though to escape notice. One seemed to break the peace, such as there was.

A covey of plant bugs flickered over a bush with delusive specks of red, vanishing when they settled.

The stream was somewhere else and we'd have to take our stuff across the mountain after all. I would go in the afternoon, sleep there if it was late, and mark the way coming back. "You'll be our guide, then," said Rafael. It was a compliment.

The tapir meat was still edible. It had been very good fresh, fried in lard with rum and tabasco sauce; and that hadn't necessarily been the best way of doing it.

One could domesticate these animals, and men could use the forest living on them, if that was desirable.

.   .   .   .

"She is in the kidneys of the forest, wringing out the mists, seeking pearls of water in the moss of the ravines, and draining away the seepage to make new torrents. She is priestess of the silence. . . .

"The Indians of these parts fear her, and she allows their hunting on the condition that they make no noise. Those who break it get nothing. . . ."

(J. E. Rivera: *La Vorágine*.)

On the long slopes of the mountain, and especially in the gorges behind, it was rare for a leaf to fall. They were dusty from the algae growing very slowly on them. The air was held in, cool, wet and nearly motionless. These were certainly the kidneys of the forest, from which the excess water seeped, perfectly clean.

It was nearly dark outside. My hand rested on something like a needle, very unexpected. A long black ant crawled from underneath; and a quarter-inch of its sting was left hanging by the tip, like a dart. The hand swelled gradually and was paralysed for two or three hours.

The animals' path seemed narrower this time and led to a blank cliff. It was lined both sides in leaf-cutting ants, empty-jawed. In the other direction it became a rivulet, feeding dwarf trees and spiny palms. They closed in around the torch beam; it seemed impossible to go any further. Beneath the sound of drips from a ravine, an animal pushed slowly in my direction. I turned the torch on, and four dark legs stepped out of the beam. The creature was a yard long in the body, strong and very clumsy. It moved on, which suited us both.

I mixed some milk in the delicious water off a rock face, and tied my hammock as close into it as possible, leaning the gun on a dry patch. There were no midges; nothing moved at all.

A twig fell in the early grey light, and four chestnut monkeys watched me get up and munch my sugar cake. Specks of white haze appeared behind them, and the gorge took on the form of rock. It was unfamiliar, ending in a low rampart of broken stone. Below this lay a quilted, still forest of many shades, with no river.

In an Indian tribe vocabulary: "—— Green. They have no word."

Not a bird flew in it, but the leaves hissed convincingly when one hurled a stone through them. Lines of blue hills lay to the right, an unknown landmark. The sugar cake wore off; and one wanted something solid.

My compass seemed to point wrong; but then the sound of the river came faintly from the wrong side too. Perhaps one might do with being completely lost more often.

The tortoise by the stream had moved thirty yards. It stood alone, under false bananas and bamboos, where the stream came towards the light. Further up, the four crags between the gorges shone in the river, appearing to shut us in.

The path over the rock was strewn with horny leaves that made me slip, as I had come in stockings for the silence. It was a mistake; spiny palm fronds lay about in the gorges without decaying. One could ruin one's feet this way.

I killed a spider monkey, which clutched the vines and cried hoarsely till the second shot. Using the skin for my feet, I dutifully searched it for parasites, and took the haunches back as they were edible.

In camp they asked justly what I had done it for. "We have plenty of meat." Besides it turned out acrid. There had been too slight reason, else I should have killed it better.

"We thought you were lost." "Oh, the guide can't get lost." "No, but he might not turn up again. One can't find a person in the woods if he misses the way."

. . . .

We cut through the mountain arums and carried our stuff across in three journeys. Butterflies came to drink the sweat from my hands when we rested in the gorge, the colour of sun-flecks, and of twilight. I was reluctant to disturb them.

The sun went out about midday and we finished moving in a hurry, as the sky sagged. A party of macaws broke away from the stream hollow and passed below us on the cliff, screeching like pebbles in a returning surf.

We spread canvases on the giant stalk of a palm frond, while Símon lit the damp wood. The rain started above the forest with a tearing noise. As the first drops came through Símon roofed the fire, using false banana leaves.

This rain pushed through the leaves and beat on the soft floor. Símon put the meat to boil during a pause, while we hoisted everything off the ground. My camera hung in a tree outside from the day before, immersed in shiny black ants, apparently camping in the case. They bit.

We ate in the dark when it was over, among the drips. A greenish point of light circled the fire occasionally and passed into the mountain forest. This was a firefly, no doubt. As half the meat was bad we ate doughnuts, with coffee and Pernod.

No fishes came when we washed our plates in the stream. It was sterile water.

As I dozed off, Rafael made sure the stores were dry. "*Guaputas!*" "What?" "Ants." I knew that. "Come!"

Leaf-cutters extended across the clearing in columns three inches thick, dividing in thin streams up some of the guy-ropes and poles, and joining from others. They passed in a continuous knot through our stores. Rice, biscuits, sugar and cassava floated along the converging streams in perfect order, and back into the forest. We burnt them to the edge of the clearing and poisoned their routes. They stayed away for two or three nights.

We said good-night to each other. "Hope you sleep."

The camp had shortcomings. All night water and cold air collected in it from the valley wall; and the sun came out late in the morning.

A few empty circles were cut in the undergrowth along the ridge-top. They were still by day, with little piles of cut leaves mouldering under the bare tree stems. Shafts of the sun came in, stirring the air slightly and ventilating the holes. A few ants ambled around the edges.

One heard nothing, but sometimes one or two went off, or came back with samples. It seemed they were keeping watch over the entire forest. Our rice could scarcely have touched ground the first day when a grain or two would have started up the valley side. It would have been assessed up here; by nightfall the work had been started.

They'd have chambers full of the mushroom on which they were known to live, and the compost with which they nourished it. Their holes indicated caverns going many yards under the clearing. Perhaps they were always ready and waiting in there for a sign of new material; and quick to learn its location.

These places were a quarter of a mile away. I didn't know of them yet.

.   .   .   .

We slept in our *ruanas*, and it was unnecessary to take them off before noon. One tended to get up late anyway. The Colombians called this cleft in the hills "Winter Place", meaning that it was always moist. The dead leaves were like sodden blotting paper, and we slipped on the stream bank.

Our cigarette smoke hung in the constantly mild air as in a room, drifting slowly into the leaves. Símon sang an interminable song about hopeless love, broken hearts, death, and so on, in a very minor key through his nose. The melody was enchanting.

Thin blackish clouds wound over the river, while the hills were wrapped in drizzle. Such days had no morning or noon; but twelve hours' even half-light. It was jade-green in the forest, lulling one's eyes. The plants seemed to merge into one another; and a leaf or twig would pass unnoticed till it touched one's face softly.

Every two trees were different, of varying heights, blending with each other in patterns as impalpable as clouds. One's route vanished behind, and there was no sense of time. One even forgot to be hungry.

There were no apparent flowers.

Blank yellow earth lay below the forest. In a few places it was exposed by a tree having slipped over, but not to the dawn, or the wind. There seldom was a dawn anyway.

When a bird shrieked or an insect flew away I no longer felt alone.

.   .   .   .

The vines on the slope from the cliff were disquieting. They lay slightly flattened against the trees, or bent through the air, linking the twigs together with short, vigorous twists. Many were greenish-grey and shiny; some had scales. One was half inclined to trust them, if they branched.

Their pale roots tapered among the boulders into the stream. I looked closely at one such every time I passed it. This ended in a bud, with two veiled eyes, and the tip wasn't quite in the water. It didn't branch. I picked it up, with a thick glove on, and it wavered stiffly in my hand. It continued to do so, by its own exertions. I lowered it as gently as possible into a canister, but it bent out again. It was entirely harmless; eventually I pushed it down tail first, though the head kept sliding out.

When one opened the tin, a foot of thin grey snake emerged, and transformed into vine-shoot. The eyes became flat spots, and the tongue a leaf-tip protruding from the bud. Half a yard more rose from the tin, as slowly as growth, and gradually sank to the ground.

CHAPTER XI

Zoology

IT was the height of the dry season out in the plain. All the clouds were hidden in here; and this was where the thunder had come from, that we had heard in San Juan de Arama beneath a clear sky.

The half-light faded; the drizzle thickened and beat heavier; it became a torrent, and the lightning struck fiercely and repeatedly, felling trees along the crests, We were protected, being low.

The stream swelled, and we heard it roaring through its boulders after the rain ceased. It remained clear, though bubbling and frothing, and by morning it had fallen quiet again.

In torch-light, the water was only a faint shadow on the sand. It supported no life; not even scum on the rocks. They were glistening white, with harsh stains of a mineral on top. The stains, sterility and bitterness of the water made me wonder what was in it—arsenic, copper . . .?

There would be iron and nothing else. The richness would have gone from the valley long ago under this rain. Now the water would be completely starved.

Very thin trees gripped the valley sides, like moss on a brick wall. One could climb hundreds of feet through them, grasping their roots, up a nearly vertical slope. The leaves intermingled, on twigs like grey wires, forming a loose, endless web. They went up thirty or forty yards, holding the air. A cocoon like a miniature lobster-pot hung from under a leaf. Allowing the constant drips to filter through, it would not become waterlogged. It was the only remains of life here.

The shoots and leaves were nearly timeless. It was always mild, wet and dim: they would grow on and on, very slowly, starving the soil.

The stream at the bottom was a turquoise wedge three foot across and five deep, pouring irresistibly through the notch it had carved. The leaf-cutting ants from the crest trickled through the cliff-forest without touching a leaf; they crossed the stream by a fallen pole, and covered a new shrub on the far side. This grew where a long tree had been undercut by the stream and slipped, trailing its vines. Nowhere else was there new growth, or decay either.

This foliage was stripped, taken back over the water, and up through the dark. The permanent trees were immune; and the ants preferred our stores, paper if wet, or even my polythene. They came an excessive distance for these things.

Through a machete-scar most of the trees leaked a substance, usually white, yellow or red, that set in the wound. One such emerged like milk, and turned blood-red in streaks as one watched it.

"False rubber," said Rafael. "The true kind doesn't grow here." All the trees would have different powers, if one only knew them.

They might each contain some poison.

Even the few leaves the leaf-cutters picked out, they gave their mushrooms to digest. It was a habit they had developed among such trees. Those they had cut over their chambers, perhaps for ventilation, were left to rot away in neat piles.

.   .   .   .

The smoke oozed out of our wet fire like grease from a

PLAIN

KING VULTURE

FROG

TRAPS

CLIFF-FOREST

SPIDER MONKEYS

STAFF OF LIFE

tube, and bent over the clearing. I was attempting to make an axe handle; Símon did it better. Soon the first white cuts showed on a thin trunk. Símon was sweating, but cheerful. The wood gave in thin springy splinters, throwing off the axe. It started to groan. "It complains," said Símon, striking harder. The trunk split gradually, and leant on the next. They were all held together by their vines. He sharpened the axe on a stone and went back there. A thin rent showed in the roof eventually, and we congratulated him.

"It's all wet here. This will bring in the sun and make it better." "It'll bring rain and midges, man." "No. Besides, they're here already."

It made no difference. There was nothing in the crowns that I had hoped to see, and we felled no more. There wasn't time. With the machete, I cut saplings whenever there was reason, and occasionally when there wasn't. It was a kind of work; and the acres of sheer vegetation frustrated me as a zoologist.

Long before I had expected to find a realm of animals over the entire wood. My task would have been to learn what they were and how they treated each other, from the necessary distance. It would have been very pleasant to explain all this to Rafael and Símon, when I had learnt it, and to have a kind of remote mastery.

There had been plans to catch tropical vipers, analyse their venom later and see how it worked; to prepare an antigen against vampire bats; to learn how insects were destroyed by their natural enemies; to collect various uncouth, primitive animals of great interest that might have lived there, or to discover the natural history of the lesser-known frogs. One had to do something like that to pass as a scientist.

The stream bent above our camp and fell some feet into a small black swamp, littered with huge rocks. This was a peculiar place that might have concealed objects of zoological interest. I caught two small whip-spiders nestling in a heap of wet boulders and brought them back. It was a moderate satisfaction.

It was necessary to confine and feed them, to observe their behaviour. In the wild they would hunt or lurk by night. If they hunted, one's footfall would alarm them; if they waited, they would be more able to than I.

We had nothing to put them in; Símon cut two pots from a section of bamboo. They were kept in by a perforated polythene cap, and rested in the shade. Their whips folded themselves neatly on each side.

The pots were glossy, hard and smooth on the outside, like dark-green enamel paint. They looked very business-like, and would allow the controlled study of other creatures. I thanked Símon; but it would be more con-vincing to have a lot of them, in case I found anything more.

.   .   .   .   .   `   .   .   .   .

The bamboos curved up in clumps; apparently one couldn't work the machete blade between them. They were as hard as ice. The sections split when cut from one side, or too savagely; and only two or three in each stem were of possible use anyway. It was a hot morning. Símon wasn't impressed.

It seemed one had to use the foot of the machete blade between the stems, keeping the tip almost still. It was a pleasure to watch him. "Like that it's easier." "Thanks, you're good at it." "I'm going to cook," he said.

Certain bamboos grew as climbers, clutching the others with stiff spines. Símon had remarked that there were a lot of them.

On the way up from the bamboo grove, there seemed to be a brown eye in the shadows. It was the under-wing of a smoky blue butterfly, as I had seen in Villavicencio. A misty patch of light showed in the pupil, and a dark line under the iris. Enclosing it were the close wavy lines that owls have round their eyes. A soft streak on the upper wing represented the ear tuft. It flew away, and I took my pots back to the camp.

. . . .

The cassava was nearly finished, and we ate rice instead. It was too pappy a food under the conditions. For some reason one wanted to eat very hard starch and a lot of it. We'd have to get some more, though San Juan seemed distant from here.

The whip-spiders had half opened their whips and poised themselves. In theory they'd have eaten some kind of small creature out of the swamp, but none lived there. They were frightened of any wasp or bee from our sugar bag, even the tiniest. One of them had a whip bitten in half by a bee. They wouldn't eat termites.

Each of the wasps in turn chewed a hole through the top and returned to the sugar. We had no flies to offer; it was one of the charms of the place.

The vine-snake was left on a bush to feed, if it could find anything. It came to no harm anyway. Composed as a vine, it altered position gradually with no visible movement. One could stare at it ten minutes, knowing it was there, and not perceive it. The Colombians agreed it was very elegant.

I smoothed the empty pots, and made notes:

SUNDAY (OR SATURDAY?)—Howls 8.30. R. saw monkeys up mountain. Later a.m.—10 or 12 collared peccary going down mountains. Habits—stood and snorted slightly in circle 10 yrds distance. Ran off. Single file Indigo pompilid (?) wasp dragging large lycosid spider long distance, circled occasionally. Took it from her. Spider limp; leg twitched $\frac{1}{2}$ hr. later. Bird (?) sticks vegetable debris on tree thorns.

It crossed my mind that this wasn't satisfactory zoology. The sun was falling and I had to shut the snake in again.

Originally we were to keep the woods round the camp for at least a hundred paces clear of hunting, in order not to disturb the animals. Rafael had thought well of this, as he liked watching creatures. Although I was the scientist, it was he who saw most of what I should have been learning; it disconcerted me at times.

We'd have a kind of sanctuary, and in time the animals would wander about disregarding us. Símon had been indifferent to the idea.

No animals lived here; still, we wouldn't hunt them. One had to be methodical. I crept off to observe them in the dusk, but splashed slightly in the invisible stream. The beach was quiet till I stepped in some army ants. There were tapir prints further down, under the vines, and I waited for them with the midges.

The stars were vanishing quickly above the river, and it was time to eat. A frog sounded from the mouth of the stream, every few minutes. Far along, another answered it. As we ate the last of the turkey, they came nearer. The topaz eye of one gleamed above the stream where it weighed down a twig. Something else to catch. Very softly I put one foot in the army ants and the other in six inches of water, as the frog dived in.

.   .   .   .

We began to consider hunting more seriously, as our meat was finished.

"One can hunt on the beach by night; not in the forest." The hunting torch was gone, however. It had been on a tree where I'd slept in the gorge: perhaps one of the four monkeys had taken it, as diversion in a quiet life.

It seemed I might have to manage with less nature-study by night. This was not too serious, for one couldn't see the environment. We had coffee: I pulled a tick and a late ant from my leg. "You're lucky," said Símon. "They get tired half-way up." Rafael said my Spanish was improving anyway.

A thick vine near by looped so low between two trees that one could use it as a privy seat. It was free of ants, which helped. The grey trees seemed to move under the shadows of those nearer as one swept the torch beam over them. The illusion was very convincing.

There were no drips at present, but it was like the floor of a cave. The trees were pale, smooth and nearly as close as stalagmites; and may not have grown much faster. They were powerful, holding their leaves beyond the torch beam and occasionally forming huge seeds, fed by little more than rain-water.

A long-nosed yellow animal crawled on the branch overhead; it was an opossum such as I'd promised to kill for some university research. Símon brought the gun, and I shot the head, which wasn't required. The animal ran and bit though its brain was destroyed. The rain began. The dead thing was finished off and preserved eventually. As a female with an embryo in the pouch, it would be of use, no doubt. There was some question of the embryonic number of teeth.

The life of the forest was not this. Some of it was in the dead bark that the termites never ate; some in the rain tapping on our canvas, and maintaining pale cream orchids on certain tree-trunks; even in the light, such as there was, and the still air. It was what we didn't collect.

.   .   .   .

Rafael and Símon took the guns so that I could collect more creatures. It was a soggy morning; the midge bites itched. Esperanza followed me about the hollow, yapping excitedly, and whining in a high pitch when the maggots in her back turned. She trembled and looked at me when I cut a switch, but merely hung back a little. She was thin and soaking wet, with nervous eyes; one couldn't easily hit her.

A yellow scorpion was hidden in a dead log. It ran with jerky, scrabbling movements among the decaying chips, round and round. It had its tail upright, the end crooked over with a curved sting folded back in a groove. When I pressed the flat body down this tail lashed against my stick, hooking the sting into it every time. Símon had caught me one of these already, explaining that one picked them up by the tip. After holding it down with the flat of a knife, this was quite safe and easy; ten minutes later I stopped shaking.

It wouldn't rest in the bamboo pot till covered from all light. These things had been on land three times longer than the mountains. They were mindless, clumsy and almost blind; still it had frightened me.

It scrabbled impotently when I tapped the pot. There was no point in having it there.

The sun came at noon. It stirred the woods and a butterfly moved over the stream, its wings a single blaze of electric blue. It continued to reappear among the vines, probably looking for its food-plant. It seemed like a companion, from its radiance. Apart from that, anything so delicate that could live in this place deserved respect.

I caught a half-grown bird-eating spider from a pad of moss on the cliff. The empty pots were still too ragged to shut, so I transferred a whip-spider to the scorpion's pot. The new thing made a silk tunnel and went into a coma at the bottom of it.

When Rafael and Símon came back, they remarked that we should have to starve. Before there had been turkeys near a beach further up; they had all gone.

CHAPTER XII

Survival

A DEER stood at the far edge of an ants' clearing. It looked as insubstantial as a leaf, behind a broken shaft of sunlight. Apparently it had not seen a person before, for it was unafraid. I fired carefully at the head, thinking to kill before it knew. The animal burst away because I had loaded with shot instead of ball.

There was a drip of blood on the arums. The deer escaped twice more from dark places on the slope; there was no further sign of it all morning.

It would be blinded in one eye, and have a raw messy wound full of shot over the whole face. Perhaps a jaguar would kill it reasonably soon, but more likely the wound would turn septic.

I had to tell Rafael and Símon in case they could help track it down. Only Símon was going to San Juan for cassava. There was little chance anyway. "It'll go to the river to drink, but far off. We have lost the best meat."

"It's a pity," said Rafael, from the other point of view.

There was a second drip near the first, but no other trace. The gun proved accurate on a tree: white drops of latex started from the patch of ripped wood. It began to drizzle.

A grey fly followed me through the steep forest for sweat. At the bottom, an orchid gripped the rock with twisted white roots, swaying over the ribbed water. The deer might have come here.

It was nearly dusk; one couldn't get out of the valley

any later. A turkey clucked where I was crawling through low trees on the rock. It wobbled on a twig in easy range, and then its underside showed in a bush down the slope. It clucked once without breath as I picked it up.

Weird bulbous plants grew on the slipped trees that I crept down. They weren't my concern. It was a good thing to have the turkey.

Rafael said there was no hope; the deer would be twenty kilometres away, having only a surface wound. "It's better to fire at the heart."

.   .   .   .

The drips seeping through the shelter of cracked leaves hissed on the fire like drum-taps.

My captive scorpion twitched the remains of a whip-spider in its maw, pushing them in with the joints of its front end. The confined shade suited it; it could sting and eat animals more alert than itself.

There was no place in the woods where a live scorpion was clearly needed; so it was best killed and preserved. It walked steadily round the killing bottle for two hours, and still moved weakly at midnight. The cyanide would stifle anything else in thirty seconds: the scorpion's pace of life was extremely slow. It moved like an automaton and went slack when it stopped.

It was a deep animal of the twilight. Where scarcely anything else lived, it would hunt, perhaps aimlessly, sustained with very little. It kept no watch, and there was nothing to watch. The quick army ants and river-side birds would starve in here.

Símon didn't come all next day. We missed him, for he was agreeable, and Rafael didn't cook so well, in my opinion. In the evening I came back from the cliff with a second turkey. Its companion had gone down the gorge clucking in apparent distress. As the sun fell, I suffered a peculiar despair for half an hour, perhaps on account of the maimed deer. It was as if one were dying.

Símon had returned a different way, along the far bank of the river. There was nothing to eat in San Juan at all. "The people are starving." "What's the matter there?" "Nothing. They don't work." He had a few green plantains from his orchard. They tasted like boiled balsa-wood, but that was fair enough in the circumstances.

"Perhaps we do better here, then." "Yes, but you hunt all day for it." "We all hunt a bit," I answered.

"Besides, we're wet all the time; it's hard living here." Rafael said there were much worse places.

Esperanza chewed the turkey bones, often frustrated in the dark. She still had the warble fly. Símon said a remedy grew in the plain, but he hadn't had time to collect any.

"Lousy cigar. It's wet too." He went to bed with it, the point shining at long intervals behind his mosquito net. Rafael stood for a while, and looked at the blank forest. "Good night, then," he said to me.

A long black ant, similar to that on which I had once put my hand, approached the fire. It patrolled placidly, shunned by all other insects. Such ants came seldom, by themselves; we saw them by candlelight and kept away. Rafael had said my hand wasn't really stung. "It gives a fever and one doesn't walk. Lasts a day or two."

It was barely possible to crush them; but they were perfectly calm and wouldn't have stung without need. I'd had sufficient of the venom not to sit on one.

They belonged to the shade, like the scorpion. Catching and needing little, they stalked deliberately over furlongs of starved forest. Just once, ten of them were filing out of a hollow, but I didn't disturb it.

Cold, ancient creatures like this grew or reproduced very slowly, over the quiet days, preserved by dread.

. . . .

The morning was brilliant; at noon the electric-blue butterfly floated quickly over the vines again.

I asked how the Indians lived in the forest.

"They live well, for they live like the animals. They find many roots, wild cassava and other kinds, just like a peccary." "They eat a lot of filth too: all kinds of vermin and worms."

"Whatever can be eaten, they eat."

The wind must have changed outside, for the sun came through all week. Símon went to the beach in the afternoons. He sang even gloomier verses, but to increasingly gay tunes, till a day when he hit his head on a rock while bathing, and nearly drowned.

"They're eating a fat calf in San Juan," he said wistfully. They were inaugurating the new chapel there. "Well, here we have turkey—provided the Doctor doesn't get us lizards now instead." I'd happened to kill an iguana before finding the turkey we wanted.

I was, in fact, eating all the lizard myself, and said it was very delicious. "Thanks, we'll be content with this," said Rafael.

"They'll be having dances . . ." Símon mused. "Not for the married men." "Makes no difference." "We thought you were ill, man." "I am, but not that ill," said Símon. He split a fly with a blow of the machete. All the same, he stayed and was not kept by the money.

It never became bright in the woods, but the grey, broken spaces seemed to open out. One could see a splash of light on a high branch, or the gloss of leaf, some hundred yards away. It was necessary to step high as the roots formed a loose net over the ground; and to let the machete blade cut accurately from time to time, by its own weight; but one could move without difficulty throughout the wood.

It was natural that there should be eyes in the forest searching at least as closely as my own. . . . There was the tree-frog's eye, veiled in a gold filigree by day, but black and staring at dusk, the pupil larger that a man's. It searched for insects; then the frog would leap a fathom from twig to twig, quick as an arrow. There were the hard, flat eyes of turkeys, ringed in sharp colours, their deep retinas even bigger than the frog's; the striped, bulbous eyes of wasps; and eyes, the sole indication of which was a distant alarm note when I moved.

Their gaze was sharper than mine; for with few exceptions, nothing edible here was visible.

A tree on the cliff was covered in flat thorns. One of them was a cockroach. It darted up the trunk like the trilobite of which I had dreamt, weeks ago. The shape was right, but when it had halted and tucked its legs in, again one saw only thorns. It had hairs and little knobs over its back, matching the precise texture of the bark.

To certain eyes the grey snake, wobbling like a vine-stem in one's grasp, would have been a vine. For a stronger impression in the role, it wobbled more as one held it, keeping its inert posture.

If the Indians hunted anything similar, in forests like this, they lived hard. The creatures seeking cockroaches or harmless snakes would not have obliged one kind to be absolutely invisible, and left others in plain view. One only saw what a bird or coati might fail to interpret. A withered leaf dropping from a spider's web for no reason was the spider; the stare of a single disembodied eye was a butterfly's wing.

We looked for every kind of animal we could see, as seriously as if we intended making a stew of them. This didn't happen, quite; but we still needed to watch. It was important to spare two or three lives if one was to kill a fourth; the Colombians paid as much attention to a bug, lizard or macaw while hunting as I.

Símon called them "birds" impartially, which confused me at first. Most kinds we never found again; so there was no point in naming them anyhow, except by their colouring or cries.

Some were "brave" (*guapo*): pitch black splashed with piercing red or blue. Such colours opened from a twig or bare stone, flew momentarily, and were folded again while their image was still flickering in one's eye.

Some insects and spiders were called "*tigre*", marked jazzily in red or yellow on black, never hiding. The smallest were picked out in lemon yellow; but the large kinds with fiercer spots and stripes looked the more alarming.

A few birds, whose colours blended delicately in a pattern too rich to be seen, were "royal" of their kind. Close to, the colours were vivid; from any distance they melted in the air.

These colours showed what the hunters saw, and how it appeared to them.

On a sunlit patch of cliff, a black and red butterfly appeared, circled and vanished. A spiral hieroglyphic stood out from the rock, which was the reverse of the wing. To a human eye it was no threat, and gave no illusions but sophistication and beauty. Usually, when there was no one here, this emblem must have had some meaning. There were no accidents here.

.   .   .   .

Outside, under the heavy, flat lighting of the beach, the "birds" ran abundantly, not difficult to see, while the army ants hunted blind. There were many lives, imperfectly preserved.

I was inclined to watch for vipers, though perhaps the floods would have washed any down faster than they would arrive. Drops of sweat, blinding in the glare, filled my eye. It was easier to look at the high green walls each side.

Few animals can have been quite safe here, for when I stepped near a big alligator posing as a log, it jumped as far as I did, in the other direction. It hit the water with a splash and sent up waves, fleeing.

Restraint and subtlety went with the quiet light that reigned in the woods. Life was ordinary on the beach, and possibly short. Anyway, it was too damned hot here; my feet swelled, and for all I knew they might get bitten.

It was best to hunt about forty yards in from the forest wall, looking through the silhouetted branches. There was some food for animals: a band of termites about five inches wide stretched up a sickly tree. Those marching down were fat; they were stripping a certain kind of lichen off the bark.

After a faint rustle, the spare outline of a turkey showed on a far trunk. It resembled the base of a shattered branch, but its colours were wasted against the hot sky and the head betrayed it. It was very light and dead when I picked it up, marked in shades of pure blue, grey and chestnut, flecked with silver.

This was a royal turkey; Símon killed another not far off. Two or three more drifted past our camp that afternoon.

They were thin and tough, their sharp eyes ringed in sky-blue. Some half-dozen would have hopped along the shadowy middle branches without our seeing. They went in schools of that number, their necks disguised by slender tufts, keeping far apart and silent on sky-blue legs. Only if one was shot would it give a sudden, last cry.

They had been feeding on a kind of blue berry; and would have come a long distance for it.

Leaves and possibly fruits of innumerable shades hung on the spidery white trees over the mountain. The turkeys would have to search out their berries in this endless patchwork. As there was nothing else to do I attempted painting it, from a flat stone in the mouth of the stream. The picture looked senseless, and I had to stand the midges or a cigar of Símon's all the time.

Throughout the afternoon a brown mark consisting of tiny ants, like dust on a smear of oil, edged along the branch overhead. They didn't seem to be doing anything. It was dark early and the first drops of a storm fell.

Late in the night we heard a soft whistle upstream through the rain. The Colombians said it would be a puma: they made this sound, perhaps to lure or disarm birds. "It's going away," they said. The animal would pace many miles; its quiet sobbing faded in the rain.

.   .   .   .

Símon didn't recover at once, and may have had malaria. I gave him chloroquin pills just in case. He thanked me, and somewhat timidly gave them back the next day. It was kind of me, he said, but he rather preferred the disease.

"We don't suffer much from it here." "Those who might are dead of it already," Rafael explained. The same was true of yellow fever; it was quite a healthy region unless one died.

"Well, we're used to the illness, more than to these —— pills." They produced a splitting headache; but he hoped they'd be good for me. "Thanks." "When you get the malaria, I mean."

Rafael and I hunted more for the time being, to make up for Símon's luck or skill. He had killed a turkey immediately above the cooking pot twice over, so that it had become a joke. He rested now, except to cook.

"Have more, man." "This will do." The Colombians never took more than they needed in any case.

We sorted our canvases to shelter his hammock better for a night; and he said he had recovered in the morning. "Very comfortable, thanks." "I'm glad of that," said Rafael: "My own hammock is half full." He showed us, with some amusement. "Military waterproof. It holds the water in." It was all right, though; apparently he'd slept on the ground in his *ruana*.

The storms had passed and there were no ill effects; but I began to doubt if I should ever become as well accustomed to life here as Rafael.

He'd lived "in every part" as he said; and there were no conditions hard enough to trouble him.

However, we did continue to eat; it surprised us at times. We hunted separately through every day, and by the time our meat was finished we had usually managed to get another two or three meals. Rafael considered it a good system: we couldn't have stored the food if we had killed more; and it was best to stay on one's feet.

All day our ears were stretched taut, so that any human sound seemed offensively brash. One's own foot-fall was annoying, however light, and we scarcely talked in the evenings. In this way the silence imposed itself.

.   .   .   .

It was only behind the noise of the rapids down-stream that one could move quite secretly. That was how I had killed the iguana, firing with a ball cartridge across the water, when a few were basking on a rock. Everywhere else there were alarms to avoid.

One listened for feathers among the leaves, or more often for a slight disquieted peep, and went in the other direction. If the bird were seriously disturbed its cry would echo in one's head, and to the horizon. Some-times it was repeated from a remote distance, quite faintly.

In the night, when two or three frogs drummed along a stretch of the river, the opposite happened. At any movement, they would hush.

We had to be careful in case our food paid attention to these noises. I couldn't tell: after an alarm the wood was still, as it had been before, but one no longer hoped to surprise a prey.

The vibration would have filled the air suddenly and

111

died away, scarcely possible to place in the time. It could have been an exact scale or chromatic phrase; at times a metallic clang or bleep. More often it was strident and remarkably disagreeable. A bird might sit complacently on its twig against a piece of sky, appearing too small for the noise.

When we were lucky the air throbbed in a tremor almost too deep to hear. It was untraceable, but the turkey would show through the trees. It was given away by a patch of white on the breast, and the red, roman bill.

We lived almost entirely on such birds: these heavy black ones and a small brown kind with scarlet wattles, giving a raucous croak. The iguana had had little meat, of which part was a bloodless, rubbery muscle one could scarcely chew. In any case, I never found another. The remains of this were preserved as a specimen.

The other birds were too scarce or elusive. I killed a toucan once; it served for two, and the mounted skin would have become a saleable trophy had it dried without rotting.

Rafael and Símon found a tapir, which came to lick salt in a deep hollow at half past nine every morning. They said they liked it, partly for its quietness and regularity. Also it was too heavy to shoot; some of it would have gone bad.

Our turkeys were rather conspicuous, and for some reason we thought it best to hunt them exclusively. If one came on another animal by accident, it wasn't one's affair.

When some peccaries paused to glance at me, I let them. They shuffled slightly, their dull, reflective eyes in shadow, and disappeared. One heard them for a moment, but their steps were well balanced and the hooves dropped lightly as feathers. They filed past, probably descending the ridge and using the path on the cliff downstream. It only happened twice.

The bird like a peal of soft bells was heard again in the morning, and sang for longer. One waited between the cadences, while it repeated one or two notes, and hoped it would try a third.

It was rather misty and I started late. It wasn't a successful day. Every now and then a butterfly went past, almost straight, with few pauses or none. They were brown, blue and green, some with colours that were startling or invisible, according to the position. In some the two ends of the spectrum fused in a sunset crimson or purple, perhaps to attract each other.

They flew very fast, having sharp wings and domed shoulders, or else floated without a motion of the wings, flimsy and rounded in these kinds. Either way they flew immensely far. I never saw one settle long: very seldom it might whirl up and quickly push an egg on to a leaf before continuing. They had long tongues and sipped briefly from bird-droppings.

They were extraordinarily light; indeed they were nearly all wing. All possible weight had been pared off, leaving only the means of searching through the forest, and a strict need to do so.

A little past the gorge, going inland, there was a ragged area full of low shrubs. A screeching turkey sat in them, but my hand wobbled. The bird fluttered and squawked on the ground till I got there.

Enclosing us was a braided stream of ants. They pressed the dead leaves, pouring along in bands a foot across, which divided and rejoined like a river from the Cordillera. It was best to step out between them.

I tied the bird to a vine in cleaner forest. In the evening, the end of the vine swung over a handful of feathers; and ghostly grey peccaries pattered off as I swore.

There was some doubt: Símon didn't believe the

peccaries would have taken meat; Rafael said they might have. It made little difference, we agreed.

The ants hadn't been important. "They bite, of course." There were ants called *tambochas*, with a serious reputation. "They're different; there are sometimes a lot of them." They didn't flourish in here.

CHAPTER XIII

Reasons for the Silence

THERE may never have been a person behind the gorges till now. Had any come, they'd have left scant impression, even for their time.

I had cut a path in through a strip of false banana plants, probably swamped from the gorges every year. The stems were chiefly water and thudded down at a stroke, most enjoyably. In a few months the suckers would reach up again, ten or twenty feet, sealing the trail.

The machete recoiled from the trees further on, vibrating at each blow. One could save breath.

This was the forest I'd seen after sleeping in the ravine. It was nearly flat, and darker than the hills. The soil may have been less poor, but heavy grey roots gripped it completely. A little stream wandered through a yard below ground level in a vertical trench, crabbed and penned in by the trees. One could see a long way under them, standing in the stream. A grey animal flickered through a patch of light in the distance, as at the end of a tunnel. It was too dark for growth down here; the few leaves were stiff and almost permanent.

The stream went dry where twenty spiders made a common web. They worked on, catching sun-specks.

The water came up again on white sand. Long floppy leaves hung over, which one folded to drink from. It was pleasant; only the peccaries had scattered a few droppings in the stream bed. One was frightened of catching their worms.

There was a bit more light, with vines hanging in it, and five caterpillars chewing an emaciated bush. They were banded black and white, with warts all over: birds and hunting wasps must have seen them easily, and left them alone.

One scarcely ever found a caterpillar, although there were butterflies, so I looked for more of their leaf to help rear them. It grew nowhere else.

One of the shade ants hunted near by, more than an inch long. It was heavy-jawed and armoured, walking quite slowly by itself. It inspired respect.

On looking near there were countless sorts of leaf. They were all dark, smooth-edged and pointed, so one failed to notice this most of the time. The caterpillars ate no sort but their own; I took two and tried feeding them. The stuff in every kind was only for a creature that lived on nothing else. Perhaps it would have poisoned any other.

This was the cause of the butterflies' constant search. They spaced their broods on separate plants, usually one or two eggs on each. It gave the best chance against caterpillar hunters; but each kind of plant they needed was hard to seek.

They knew the forest better than man, as one should expect. We had to go far ourselves, in spite of our supplies.

Every few minutes the light and the apparent weight of the air changed. The top leaves might show through as if dotted on the sky, or, sometimes, dark palm-fronds scraped above one's hair. The wood never repeated itself exactly; and one hoped there was a patch where the turkeys fed. One might as soon find a vine sprouting peso notes, but all hunting animals kept on the move.

It was quiet because no creature held ground; none could have held enough to feed in. Even where there was new growth or fruit, it didn't last. The animals that fed in such places united, having nothing to keep from each other; and went quickly. They'd have learnt where the best places were that way. Those that knew most, like the leaf-cutters and perhaps the howling monkeys, kept a tribal ground.

There weren't many in the wood, however they lived. Four ants guarded a dozen scale insects on a herb; they'd have got licks of sugary stuff from the insects, but very little. A wasp stung me in the neck when I had passed her nest going back. It showed how quiet these woods were; she was the only one.

．　．　．　．　．　．　．　．　．　．　．　．

Símon said "Ah, misery!" with gusto. "Life," he explained; and asked me to get him an orchid for his young wife, if I happened to see any. Rafael and he were going back for plantains or cassava in a few days.

There was a noise of two harp-strings; Símon said it was a cicada. It went over us quickly, the wings clicking like dry leaves. "Rain coming." The light faded after a puff of wind, and Símon got in his hammock. I put the vine-snake away; it hadn't caught anything. Símon sang quietly for a while and lit a cigar as the thunder approached. It still didn't rain.

"*Guaputas*. You have no girl in Colombia, Doctor? Only in England? . . . No use here."

"One wouldn't get along here that way." "No, but in San Juan. There are animals, too; any sort of chase."

The rain began, lasting till dusk. One couldn't hear oneself think. Símon finished the cigar and sang for forty minutes, probably to keep himself company. His tune, if any, was drowned in the storm.

Rafael came back in the dark, relatively dry, with a fat turkey. He'd made a shelter of palm leaves against the rain. When skilfully arranged all the drips ran down the outside. "It's going to be wet, Doctor; that was our summer last week." He stood and smoked as usual, drying his hat over the fire.

There were two animals like miniature crabs he'd found in a hollow tree. He liked to know what was living in the wood; and the creatures in places like that were new to him. He'd look for others, if they still interested me.

The river began to roar. Dim patches of foam gleamed in it, probably over sunken rocks. No stars or anything else could be seen; from now on the river grew more quickly and was louder from each successive storm. Between times it died down again.

We talked more because of the past noise, and finished the rum. Rafael told a story about a bandit and a snake, which I didn't follow. I believe the bandit had cut his own foot off, and lived.

This had been away in the Cordillera, some years ago. It seemed the snakes always lived in settled country and around the farms, though not for the company.

In these places there was new or decaying growth of weeds and crops; and the snakes lived on its rapid destruction, taking up insects, lizards, frogs and rodents with great economy of effort.

"I don't like to leave one living," said Rafael, who came from that country.

The sky was deeper blue in the morning; the dust from the plain that usually made a greenish tint had been washed down.

Across the river, perched on the steep rock where the iguanas had lain, was a new sort of wood, with stunted trees. The ground was black and greasy, leading to the foot of a wet cliff, and half the trees were dead. They lay over rivulets the colour of black treacle; army ants scurried along them. The air stank rather, and was reasonably stocked with both midges and mosquitoes. Many of the plants had stinging ants inside; and the rest were climbing bamboos, forming a low spiked trellis. An orchid drooped over a stream, well removed from any likely admiration.

I picked it for Símon. He thanked me after, but really wanted a bulb.

Beyond was a steep meadow lying in a bay of forest. It was just inside the high grass crest known as "The Blade of Fate" that separated the forest from the plain. From there on the land was used by men.

The Colombians said if one fired such a meadow and waited a few nights later, animals came to eat the new shoots. Hunting like that, the Indians could have singed the forest from far in the East, back to this crest. Further in, the storms and drizzle would have stopped them.

The pallid grass, the stinking low growth alongside, and the black water were fair signs of a burnt or sickly ground. This would have been the farthest salient of any human culture. Nobody knew of men coming here; and it was apparently beginning to pick up again.

The sun was low and birds piped from the trees beyond. The breeze carried a scent over from some tree, rather like apricots. Downhill the river ran in the folds of forest like a blue snake. One could see how it had scratched itself in.

It was true that the far mountainside hung from its trees, and so did all the slopes. The trees had held them in the air as the river sank in around them.

The trees were hard and dark all through. Because of the mild weather they lived long; each kind lasted among the others, stitching the country a bit closer. Except along the river nothing would kill them and they matured eventually—no matter how long it took.

In a sense every creature here had to live this way. It was a good country for patience.

I went into clean forest at the bottom of the meadow, where there was a cliff cut by an earlier bend of the river. It was the kind of wood we were used to by now, intricate and muted from the passage of time. The riverside tangle and the more demanding animals had long since died away. Man would have left first, if he'd been there.

A very big caterpillar was stretched on a vine, its yellow bands shining in semi-darkness. It resembled the snakes I had day-dreamt, so I looked for another of these vines to help rear it. Naturally there wasn't another.

I shot a turkey above the river, collected it, and crossed to our stream mouth in the short twilight. Long grey fish held themselves in line with the current.

Símon said the turkey wasn't good to eat. Having dropped it dead in the river from as close as possible and then dived after, I said we'd try it, though he was free. There was no difference from the other black ones, only it was thinner, with a longer tail. It did us no harm.

.   .   .   .

One had an odd sensation of not being one's own size in the hammock. It went off, in time. I listened to the water roaring like a strong wind, and remembered a storm in the night when the leaf-cutters had come again.

The Colombians returned from the river; they couldn't cross to go to San Juan. More clouds hung over, as well. It seemed we'd be eating our shoes.

"How would you wish those cooked?" The joke was used up, but I said roasted.

An object like a long strip of wet liquorice looped itself slowly over the clearing. It was banded black and orange, in a herringbone pattern, and had no head. The front end stretched up a few inches, waving in the air at me. "What the hell is this?" I was feeling a bit odd and didn't like it. "Oh, a worm." We kept it as a specimen.

I took coffee and chloroquin, and lay down again. One could avoid malaria on two pills a fortnight, but it had been interesting to see how long one did without them.

The Colombians left in the afternoon. The forest was entirely mine, being almost unknown. Some oil geologists had once passed a little way south, remarking tersely: "9 m. Cgl. Sst."; but no one else. It had attracted me a few weeks before. Now I began to wonder: if others hadn't come near this place, weren't they sensible? One only got silence, and a head like a bad tooth.

The quiet was that of extreme poverty. Few talents were necessary to live here: the striped worm could merely smell, creep and distinguish light from darkness. It had a hole on the bottom instead of a mouth and couldn't bite.

Only it made no difference how ingenious a creature might be: there was no soft living here. The worm smelt food from a long distance, and was tough. Others of the same kind, found in rich waters, are flat and glide gently on their slime; this one was full of cold muscle, hunching itself up and covering the ground at a fair pace.

There was nothing to spare, dead or alive. The markings of the worm suggested poison; it was like an orange leaf with black veins and spots. Only a creature of very special tastes would have tried it; and all the venomous animals were marked differently. Our turkeys were apparently of this kind. It was because they were slow and obtrusive that we had been able to kill them; without cooking we should probably have regretted it.

The innocuous animals were burnt into the texture of the forest, or into the air. They were scattered, often on particular plants they resembled, and couldn't be hunted casually. Each would have had its own hunter, if any, and its food. There was little disturbance: they kept searching.

This was the cause of the silence—"Those who break it get nothing." We never smelt carrion or saw a vulture in here: there was hardly any violence.

We had survived a few weeks, shooting the turkeys faster than they had bred, and doing little else.

The storm that night was appalling. When one expected the rain to give out of its own fury, it grew heavier. It seemed capable of crushing the trees eventually, but that was improbable.

Next day to my extreme surprise, I felt even worse. All the bones jarred on each other; and one's nerves were too excitable. It was an odd effect of the little white things splitting themselves innocently in one's blood.

The quiet of the wood seemed like that of a creature in reasonable health. Every bit of life checked or supported one or two others; nothing grew to excess or lacked a chance. I appeared to have been something of a tumour, having killed too much, and once badly, for ambitions the place wouldn't sustain.

Perhaps one should have taken life more as it came, for one couldn't attempt any mastery of it here without being ridiculous. Nothing was more absurd than considering how a tortoise or puma lived, unless there were occasion to try it oneself. Besides, there could be no sharper test of what really mattered.

This was the benign fever, but I preferred chloroquin ("Aralen"). The Winthrop Company, the manufacturers of this drug, certainly save more lives at a tolerable price than most charities do for love.

We had three hammocks, each of them uncomfortable in its own way. For relief there was a vista of blackish leaves in the rain. The worm had squeezed out of its pot and gone.

The rain stopped by the second or third morning, and I was a good bit thinner. There was a cooked turkey, which needed more boiling to be safe. It would be foolish to shirk lighting the fire, and as I realized, cowardly.

The Colombians came back as I was blowing at the

sticks; they'd camped on the far bank somehow, waiting for the river to fall. It had still been up to their necks when they crossed.

It was suggested that we returned to Plaza Bonita, the first camp. I was reluctant to do this, because although we found little here, its value was clearer. The Colombians pointed out that it wasn't healthy for me. That was my affair; but I'd be rather heavy to carry up the cliff if I died. It was a touching argument. "Have to get that path round," I said.

There wasn't time to live here anyway, and I faced a lot of trouble for having no specimens or information.

Rafael went to clear the trail. Esperanza was whining more than before: we held her and squeezed the maggots out. They were in septic cavities of the back muscle, and one forced them through their breathing holes. Símon got himself bitten and I was sick. Esperanza ran in circles howling; "It'll make you a prettier girl," said Símon hopefully. So it did.

The sun rose next day. Apparently the tapir had been coming for its salt all this time; at least it was there again. I went to see it, just for once. One had to be very quiet, but it let us approach within ten yards. It was wet and rather dirty, with bald flanks. It sniffed a leaf in the swamp and turned its black eye round at us. Its snout bent our way for a moment, but it wasn't concerned.

It might have had warble-fly maggots, and I wanted to track these down at any cost now; but as Rafael said, we had to leave this animal in peace.

Considering everything, I carried a fair amount back.

CHAPTER XIV

Society

THE gorge stayed as silent as ever the last time we rested there, but green leaves were streaming down the bark of a tree in the middle. It had come in season for the ants, or was getting feeble; they had picked it out. They carried much smaller ants up on their backs, which worked above somehow and rode the leaf fragments down. Each side of the gorge the other, darker foliage hung still as this was quietly rushed inland.

In a few days, after we had gone, the clouds would be settling for the year. The starch would drain from the leaves, and the ants' mushroom wouldn't grow so well. Perhaps they were stocking up this fortnight; they took anything innocuous they could get. I found a forlorn party of them stripping the wet paper off my soap at midnight.

Beyond the gorge, we saw patches of the green, dusty sky of the plain. It was half-way back to the world of men. We came down to the region of natural destruction and new growth along the river. Files of large red and grey ants were still working over our clearing. They foraged intelligently, and we sat at a little distance from them, smoking and enjoying the dry air off the beach. The ants were *tambochas,* that grow too numerous along the big rivers, and may have eaten people at times. They were rather decorative here, like strings of moving beads.

Downstream, two eagles patrolled the hot stones, possibly for lizards. Their wings were nearly motionless, delicately curved by their weight hanging between the tips, and they pivoted on three feathers at the end of each sweep.

Occasionally we passed a vulture waiting on a branch. These birds didn't live in the silent forest behind, because there was too little opportunity there.

The floods, which would tear up or drown parts of the riverside most years, enriched it when they went down. Exquisitely light fluff carrying the seed of a quick-growing tree drifted through our clearing continually; and a haze of seedlings had risen three feet from the ground while we were away.

We cleared the ground and settled as usual. I persecuted several ticks off my skin; the country was much livelier. Hundreds of caterpillars ate a dry, feathery bush on the beach outside, where we collected firewood.

The new growth choked itself, and was eaten by bugs and grasshoppers over the still ribbons of army ants. There was only a small fringe of it.

In parts of the plain and along the big rivers, where there were heavy floods or old farms, this growth would extend over miles. The large herds of white-lipped peccaries ran there, tick-ridden, dangerous, and seen off only by the occasional plague of *tambochas,* if at all. These were the places for snakes, jaguars and vampire bats, it was said. People lived there, as it was relatively rich; so the life of the plain had a fierce reputation. I never saw these things myself.

Símon caught some large tasteless fishes with paired fangs, like the canines of a fox. I asked if they'd bite. "Sure," he said. "In warmer waters they hold on, while the *caribes* come to cut you up. These get some of the pieces." One would hope so.

.   .   .   .

In the evening a party of macaws settled on the wall of

the forest, squawking over a kind of fruit. I killed one, partly for food, and partly to mount the skin and sell it. My only deep regret is making a mess of the skin; for it was as suitable a bird to eat as a small turkey.

Several kinds of fruit and seed were ripening, mostly rather forbidding. We ate a sort of guava from one of the trees. It tasted refreshing, but was mainly pips. Símon was more interested than us in these things; he showed one rather repellent pod to Rafael, who looked down his nose and said "What was it?"

"Poison—I think."

After all, he was staying in the region, and we weren't.

Animals came, probably from far inland. They weren't conspicuous: seven peccaries crossed the rock to the island at noon; a tree-rat barked by night; monkeys could be heard dropping shells in a thick mass of vines.

It was too easy most days to kill enough meat, and the undertaking to get specimens occupied me. Nothing would seem more important than having enough material for study in the laboratory at Villavicencio.

I killed eleven animals, including three monkeys, and found twice as many kinds of parasite. In several of the animals there weren't any. The killing was technically not bad; one made sure of the heart, and cracked the skull immediately the animal dropped.

A flock of black and yellow birds, spread round in the trees, started hooting as I rested on a log with a dead coati. The two pure notes, repeated again and again, grew intolerable. They were doubtless hooting the coati, a hunter of birds mainly. The noise stopped one thinking at the time. They pursued us through increasingly dirty forest into a palisade of canes. I stepped on to the beach among the blind army ants.

Símon's wife was ill; he'd taken penicillin back for her, and Rafael had gone with him to fetch provisions if Símon couldn't return.

There wasn't so much as a thread-worm in the coati; one couldn't have destroyed a healthier animal. While skinning it, I abruptly lost the sense of caring for anything. People were apt to say "One must have shame": this was the lack of it. It was an interesting state of mind, which would explain certain acts during the war, of which I'd heard. It came partly from tiredness and the heat.

For at least an hour I concentrated on killing the one or two midges in my hammock, for lack of anything better to do. The idea was to sleep.

A blue wasp dragged a spider over the clearing, buzzing angrily when it got stuck. She went on and on, as the sun fell. It occurred to me that life was hard in the tropics.

My friends came back and we had supper. Símon's wife was recovering, and a neighbour was looking after her.

I finished skinning the animal, snipping the joints in its paws, and as soon as possible left the skin to dry on the beach next day. A bright golden light flashed over the water.

It began to rain, and one or two of the lights appeared in camp. They were long grey beetles, with two yellow-shining patches on the shoulders, and green on the abdomen, glowing when they landed. I picked one up and watched the gold light flicker under its nerve impulses. The insect manœuvred itself to bite my thumb and flew winking into the rain.

Some friends of Símon (as I was glad to learn) came after a few days. Where was he? Oh, he was out hunting somewhere; how were things in San Juan? "All right. His wife is worse." They went to try their luck down-river.

My companions came back with two peccaries, and I met them along the path, just in case. He had arranged the visit and would go back with them. We said no more of the matter.

"Let's talk of something else. It will interest you: an animal nearly killed me at last." Rafael had mortally wounded the male, but it rushed Símon abruptly when its mate fell. "Don Rafael hits it, yet it attacks me." He thought this unreasonable.

"On account of your killing its female." "Very savage. There would have been others."

We laughed a bit and hung the two animals from a bough outside to skin. They were impressive, weighing about seventy pounds each, supported by whatever they had been able to find on the forest floor.

Unusually aggressive wasps settled on the carcass, and the skinning was awkward in the sun. One wants a blunt-edged knife for some of this work; I may have reduced the value of one hide by pesos, and regret it if so.

Símon and his friends left with most of the meat and the hides after a period of bargaining. It seemed more peaceful. Outside, the stones of the beach glowed blood-red, before the first fireflies came.

"I prefer it without a lot of people," observed Rafael.

We ate and I made preservative for the peccary parasites. The animals had certain worms and lice habitually, in very moderate numbers. Grey jelly-like flukes started creeping out of the hearts when I opened them. There were four or five in each, gliding around quite harmlessly. They were the most secure and comfortable beings I'd ever noticed.

The animals were healthy, because there weren't too many.

.   .   .   .

In the morning I killed a deer, making no mistake over my aim.

Símon had brought a friend, Policarpo Gonsalez, who was to take over from him. He didn't want to chat about his wife merely for etiquette, and said cheerfully that she was dying. "Where are my cigars, damn it?"

We searched for the deer before he left. "A cat will have carried it off," they said. It had been some way from the beach, among high grey trees and a few palms, along a dry creek. The landmarks were ambiguous now, and it would have been better to mark the trail. We never proved what had happened.

Its huge eye had glanced at me quite casually, as it finished studying a palm-heart, and it had stepped back one pace, remaining in view. It scarcely even looked at me. Finding the carcass would not have made me happy.

After this, two large parties, of coati and of squirrel monkeys, went by our camp; and I killed one of each. We didn't seek any more animals for science. These two, both reasonably infested and one diseased, made the collection enough for an expert to examine, if he chose.

Símon left, and Polo settled in as if he were used to it. He had lived in San Juan all his life, but it was nearly as comfortable here.

Scarlet ibis came to the sandbars in the river, and Polo ran to look at them first. He was about sixteen, but only a dead man would not be excited by them.

Their long bills were used to search for some creature round the edge of the white sand. They stood like deep flames, colouring the sand and the water; there were ten or fifteen of them.

Their wings flashed pink, probably warning one another, and they remained distant from me. Visiting the sandbars of every river, they were apt to be killed for their beauty. As Rafael and Polo said, we didn't need to do that.

One morning a moth flew along the beach, bearing lazy lines of rich emerald against black. The brilliance of light shining through a young palm frond would match it; but it went on swiftly. It was one of the few moths that fly hundreds of miles.

This nearly magical beauty showed the flight over dangerous expanses, for a thin living. It was in the hummingbirds, and perhaps in the deer.

That evening Polo brought down the squirrel monkey, as it had stuck in a rather difficult tree which I couldn't manage. It had minute pink nails like a man's. "It's very pretty," he said. I preserved its many thread-worms, and that was the end.

The extreme gentleness of the woods abased me. Many kinds of wasp and bee lived on our food without stinging us or chivvying each other. We could brush them off as if they were butterflies, and on coming back each settled quietly in its place.

We were surrounded by leaf-cutting ants just now, not one of which bit us. They avoided each other courteously where their columns crossed.

Twice a shade-ant, having a day's fever in its sting, crawled up my trouser-leg and was shaken down again without my even knowing it. One could sleep in the open among the insects and not be hurt, for each pursued its craft exclusively. The midges didn't count, belonging to the fiercer world of the beach. Rafael got a warble-fly in his neck; he left a plaster on the breathing hole and extracted it when the itching stopped.

"That way it can't breathe. It moved at first under the plaster and the itching was very bad. Curious things."

The bigger animals, such as I'd killed, were even more gentle than the forest insects. This period was rather like a festival; and the stomach of a spider monkey was full of crimson fruit pulp. A squirrel danced on a tree in the morning light, its tail like a stream of gold dust.

They would have had to conceal themselves or make threats when a jaguar or some hawk came near. Yet this would hardly ever happen. They were not the least bit furtive, but went calmly, often rather preoccupied.

For months at a time they lived by studying the forest and going where there was a little food. They couldn't take one another's, having different experience, instincts and needs. It had been rather stupid bringing the standards of our own struggle for success into the forest.

There wasn't much intelligence of the human kind, because there was seldom an opportunity to seize on anything new. Probably the squirrel had been practising its leaps and balance, and explored the laws of motion with its tail.

We had been confined by necessity ourselves most of the time. The curious thing is one couldn't resent it, or regret the ease we were missing.

In the animals of this place, confined by the strictest laws, there was often something unaccountable. The wings of the black and green moth were edged in snow-white hairs about a millimetre long, without which it would have been a mere reflection of the background. The spiders inland inhabited a single web and were hungry, without eating one another.

Three gigantic white vultures had gathered on a dead peccary in the forest at midday, without any other scavenger seeing them to compete. They had floated down from mid-air, concealed against the clouds. This was not only obeying necessity, but discovering it.

. . . .

The midges no longer bit if one sat a little way from the candle. Practically all had settled in great clusters on a kind of herb in the clearing. I thoughtfully dusted them with DDT. We never noticed much difference.

It was necessary to sit in the smoke by day, and to keep the fire going for it.

Our protection was crude: the Indians must have discovered that tobacco leaves were best for this long before the earliest pipe or cigar, the dim ceremonies in the forest and the artificial sense of peace. However, we hadn't any.

I spent the last few days collecting leaves deliberately. Most of the forest was certainly inedible, and some of the leaves the midges never settled on and the leaf-cutters always shunned may have been unpleasant to them.

A small glossy leaf near the camp stank very strongly of citronella, but one could scarcely tell what an insect would scent, or from how far. Our own repellent was odourless. It worked all right, but stung the lips and cost money.

These leaves were a sign of the weather. Even near the beach they were mostly long, smooth and even; there were never strong winds or droughts that would wither them or break them up. The only sign of stress was that some grew like the fingers of a hand on the tip of their stem, as if grasping the light. This was mostly near the beach, where the shade was broken.

Further in there was no sign of competition. Every tree survived indefinitely with the other kinds that wouldn't starve it. There would have been two or three hundred kinds of tree. For as long as the big ones lived, there was no change; and then only bit by bit as they died over the centuries. Presumably each of the peculiar seeds would have its place and time, but most often they came to nothing, leaving the grey spaces between the trunks.

The leaves here were difficult to distinguish from each other. I made a mistake choosing the obvious ones on the new land. One can probably tell what leaves are most likely to be active, from the time they live and the way they grow. Those on the old ground were probably the best protected.

Anyway, it was nice, quiet work; and of a sort which may be useful eventually. Only the animals know, in a sense, what is in this kind of forest; nobody knows how to use it. Even the Indians usually find richer places.

It was poor land; the creatures lived on extremely little, and with difficulty. Before we left, Polo showed me howler monkeys biting off rock on the far bank. "For lime," he explained.

"Don't shoot them." "No."

I learnt why the ground was often bare under the trees with stinging ants: they were growing on leaf-cutters' nests. The leaf-cutters had killed everything else, leaving this kind free. There would have been glands in the tree, on which the stinging ants fed. Elsewhere, when the tree was shaded over or grew old, the stinging ants seemed to go. Probably the glands dried up. The leaf-cutters were attacking one of these old ones in preference to anything else; it was finished.

It took all night to label and pack the leaves and specimens. The remaining Pernod was invaluable. It made a bright red ink when used to eke out the black, and one could etch with it directly on the leaves. It was a good drink too.

Símon brought horses, and I rode back, having stepped on a spiny palm-frond that morning. The ride was a new experience for me and the horse, otherwise used to hard circumstances.

When I could walk again we had a farewell party with Símon. His wife went to bed early. Apparently she was recovering. "But if she doesn't?"

"Get another."

"Very bad man, this," remarked Rafael. Símon grinned.

My point had been to send medicines if need be; apparently that was unnecessary as he could have them sent. If a doctor were needed, he knew I couldn't afford it anyway. As for his reply, in the circumstances it was true, he said.

"One doesn't live alone, man."

In Villavicencio I caught flies and found they were attracted to all the leaf extracts in turn, though sometimes they died abruptly. The technique was crude.

Carlos asked what I was doing and suggested one or two other things to look for.

"My father went hunting with a tourist once, and it was very hot. The man chewed a leaf for his thirst, and in a quarter of an hour three of his front teeth dropped out. They went back to look for the leaf, because it might be valuable to dentists. They never found it." I've heard of this plant since.

Rafael and Carlos with some friends gave me a send-off from one of the cafés.

"You should talk at a party, Don Stéban." "I'm thinking." "Tell it then." The speech and manners here let one discuss anything, even if it were true.

This was a deliberate art. "We don't like to step on each other's feet," said Carlos. "Nor to have it done to us." At the same time, they learnt what men did, with very few illusions.

". . . but that one talks a lot of straw."

I left them at the gate of the Institute, and promised to return from England as soon as possible.

At home, the chief men were putting up enormous faceless buildings, apparently to look big. The houses and the older women were laden with objects of ritual wealth, which were believed necessary. There was a smell of fear. An important or qualified person performed little manual effort and never got dirty in his public role.

Someone drowned in the Serpentine, apparently surrounded by a large crowd who were sunning themselves. One hated to be conspicuous.

I soon lost the perception of others that was customary in the plain, and have grown frightened of the poverty of such difficult country. It is more comfortable for us to inhabit our shadow-world, which has much in common with childhood. Its rules and images are simpler to follow than life, and it is well nourished.

It seems natural for the people who come easily into safe positions to be little developed. The habits of the dark past can be carried on anywhere rich enough; it is on the frontiers that one needs to understand most.

Only the least pretentious of us can live there, and the monkeys are probably still ahead.

NOTES

NOTES (1)

Particular Animals

Alligators—Alligatoridae in general.

Animals "like miniature crabs"—*Gonoleptidae* (primitive 118
    Opiliones): two species or dimorphic species.
    Very clumsy-looking.

ANTS—Army; in ribbons or columns along beach—
    Eciton.
    Braided like river . . .—also *Eciton* different species. 113
       It was a very big army, but I only found one in
       six weeks. These enormous colonies, like those
       of leaf-cutting ants and higher termites, are
       super-societies, occupying as much ground as a
       great many normal ant societies, and with
       queens as big as sausages.
       Leaf-cutting—*Atta,* probably *cephalotes.*
       Workers of a small caste were removing some-
       thing like bad fungus from their nest on one
       occasion, and putting it carefully in a nearby
       stream. For the natural history, read Sanderson
       (1944).
    Large stinging—*Poneridae,* like *Dinoponera.* 105
       Inaccurate to call them "shade ants". Some also 116
       live in deserts. They are mostly where there is
       little food.
    Stinging in trees—*Azteca* in *Cecropia.* Similar ants in 70
       hollow-stemmed herbaceous twiner.
         Wheeler (1942) studied the role of these ants 133
       in their host plants and denied that they defend
       Cecropia from *Atta.* However he never saw *Atta*
       attack a tree with *Azteca* in it. The question is
       whether they'd attack one without *Azteca,* which
       is what I found.

Young *Cecropias* which the *Azteca* haven't occupied yet are certainly not attacked. It seems their leaves are unattractive to *Atta*, for use. This isn't necessarily true of older ones. The leaf-cutters also strip all leaves within a few yards of the ground above their nests, not for use but more likely for ventilation. This creates a clearing as the defoliated lower trees die off. At the rim of the forest these places are usually occupied by one or two old *Cecropias*, untouched, always full of *Aztecas*; and no *Cecropia* seedlings. As *Cecropia* germinates in the light it looks as if the seedlings are killed off. In this case, the older trees are defended.

I think both that the *Cecropia* seedlings are unattractive for *Atta* to use, and that the older trees are defended from them by *Azteca*.

Tambochas—Not *Eciton*.

64, 67 BEES—Black, on sugar—Also found on large bracket fungus.

Midget, sucking sweat—*Meliponinae*.

Beetles, glowing; "fireflies"—*Pyrophorus* (Elateridae).

The yellow light was apparently like that of a sodium lamp, which seems impossible.

BUTTERFLIES—

21 Striped yellow, black and red—*Danaidae* and possibly *Heliconid* mimics.

Richter observed Mullerian and Batesian mimicry hereabouts, but never in the Sierra de la Macarena. I didn't see this common pattern in the Macarena.

Blue—*Morphinae* various species, the biggest "smoky blue" being least brilliant and the smallest most so.

76 Gathering on patches of mud—*Pierinae*, some *Papilioninae*, *Catagramma* spp., dioptid moths, among others. Seven or more species in a cluster.

Salt was tried as an attractant, and didn't

work. Dead fish weren't much sought either. A patch of bacteria or algae in the mud could have yielded vitamins.

Cipher on underside—*Catagramma*. 108
Generally, butterflies were more common relative to moths and to other insects in the forest, than they are elsewhere.

CATERPILLARS—
On feathery bush on beach—Like *Lymantriidae* or 125 *Arctiidae,* the bush like *Acacia* species.

Striped black and yellow—*Pseudosphinx tetrio,* 120 parasitized by Ichneumon wasp. The parasite chewed its way out of the box some time after pupation.

Striped white and black, with warts—Typically 116 aposematic, hence not scattered separately.

Cocoon like miniature lobster pot—*Dioptidae*. 95-6

Daddy-long-legs—*Phalangidae* (Opiliones) in general. 54
Silly name, but harvestman is ambiguous.

Deer—*Mazama virginiana*.

FISH—*Caribes—Serrasalmus*. That is, the same as *Piranhas* in Brazil.

Ray; Sting-ray—*Potamotrygon*.

With paired fangs—*Cynodon* species (Characidae). 125
The most interesting fish in some ways were sucking catfish living among boulders in the rapids. They were heavily armoured and shaped exactly like some Devonian Ostracoderms. Perhaps the latter lived the same way.

FROGS—Tree—Mostly or all *Hylidae*.

Big as rat—Common in Villavicencio. 21
Also found at Plaza Bonita, but not in old forest.

Gnats, greenish-white—*Culicidae*. Apparently lacking 72 pigment and confined to forest and midnight in the same way as some cave-animals.

Grasshoppers—Nearly all *Tettigonoidea*.

INSECTS—
Ugly, flat—*Ascalaphidae* (Neuroptera) larvae— 80 (Crawling backwards).

39   Slender, like grass—Mantid.

LIZARDS—

17   Emerald Green—Iguana species. It would hardly
       ever be seen in closed forest.

28   Leaping—*Anolis.*
       Most animals between the size of the bigger
       spiders and the marmosets and tarsiers in rain-
       forests jump, if they don't fly.

66 Midges—*Simuliidae.*

38 MONKEYS—Grey-green; squirrel—*Saimiri sciurea.*
       Ate nuts and insects.
       Howler—*Alouatta seniculus.*

133   I didn't check that the rock contained lime. The
       local opinion seems very sensible.
       Spider—*Ateles belzebuth.*
       Also seen once were *Pithecia monachus,* three or
       four in a low tree.
           The societies of the two commonest species
       were about the same weight, 20 to 40 *Saimiri,*
       10 to 15 *Ateles*; and the usual five to eight
       Alouatta would weigh a little bit less. The
       Pithecia society was much smaller.

12 Newt—*Oedipus.*

Peccaries—Those seen all Collared Peccary: *Dicotyles
       tayaçu.* They go in poorer country generally than
       Tayassu (Dicotyles) labiatus.

SPIDERS—Bird eating—*Theraphosidae* in general.
       . . . No suggestion that they would eat birds,
       necessarily.

54   Crab-like—*Selenops* or other Eusparassid.

22   Heavy-bodied; hunting in field—Largish *Salticidae.*
       The hunting action is common to *Salticidae* and
       Lycosidae, which are not related closely. That
       lizards hunt the same way suggests it is useful for
       approaching flies. The image of the hunters'
       legs would snap from one group of eye-facets to
       a different group, without being registered in

those intervening. It's only a guess that this fools
the fly.

Hunting; in hut Ch III, on beach Ch VI—Big
Lycosidae.

Social—*Nephilinae.*   115

With spikes, or scalloped like dead leaf—*Gasteracan-
thinae,* several species.

Tapir—*Tapirus terrestris.*
    They're adaptable to private domestic life, but 89
    might not stand being herded.

Tree-rat—*Hystricomorphidae,* possibly *Diplomys.*   19

Turkeys—*Cracidae* in general.
    That is, not true turkeys, but ecologically
    similar.

TURKEYS—Black—*Crax* two species.
    These seem to be conspicuously coloured, slow 121
    and unwary. If generally edible without cooking,
    it's a wonder they live.
Brown, with wattles—*Penelope.*
Ground—*Ortalis.*

WASPS—Chequered, wingless—*Mutillidae.*
Spider-hunting, dark blue—*Pompilidae.*
That stung me—*Vespidae,* but apparently solitary. 117
    This happened twice.

Water-Scorpion—*Belostomatidae.*   43

Whip-Spiders—*Amblypigi* in general. The usual name
    "whip-scorpion" is useless, because also used for
    the Uropygi, quite different. It's a reasonable
    name for them.
Black—Possibly *Acanthrophrynus.*   59
    The direction-finding by rather long air-waves
    must be a function of the whips. Length is neces-
    sary to resolve long waves, as with lateral lines
    of fish.

Worm—Land Planarian. It was triangular in section, the 121
    muscles in the back enabling it to loop like a
    geometer.

NOTES (2)

Distribution of the Forest

It is about 3° N, on and around the hills of the Sierra de la Macarena, at the south-west corner of the grassland in the Eastern plain of Colombia, and some 30 km east from the Eastern chain of the Andes. The hills rise abruptly from about 300 to 1,500 metres above sea level; I stayed near the bottom.

The nearest measured rainfall is 200 cm at San Martín (Schmidt 1948), with a dry season December into March. In the forest it is higher; I have described only the dry season. This was 1955/56, rather wetter than average; all the same, the hills have strictly local storms.

The temperatures stay within a few degrees of 24° C (75° F).

The soil in the forest is mostly yellow, crumbly and featureless. Outside it is whitish and sandy over clay/iron pans, probably very old (Jenny 1949).

Along the Andes there was recently a similar forest, confined to the area of mountain rains (Bates 1948). Out in the plain are local forests that suffer as much drought as the grass. These are on recent alluvium and slopes extending far from the water, and getting as dry as the grassland if not drier. The same is true of the Amazon forests immediately south of the Macarena.

Most of these forests have sharp boundaries: there is evergreen forest up to 40 metres average height, and short grass next to it. This looks like a place which has been burnt in parts. That seems impossible, but isn't. The people in pre-Colombian times, and after, were fighting and moving around. They burnt the grass fringes for hunting. Rainforest burns after a drought, the ground carrying the fire. (C. J. W. Pitt unpubl.) Part of the Amazon forests and the islands in the plain have been cleared somehow, and the forest has re-established itself, at times in the past. The soil is relatively young. There are people in these places, farming on a small scale.

The forest of the Macarena, and in parts of Guiana, surrounded by poor grassland, is probably unburnt; and outside where burning was not prevented by dry-season storms, forest could not establish itself before the next fire. The soil was too old to stand clearing. Hardly anyone can live in these places.

NOTES (3)

Character of the Forest

I THINK the quality of the interior rain-forest is due to the immense stretches of time that pass with little disturbance there. The fringes and river banks are quite different. It takes time for anything to become organized, and the quietness of the forest allows forms and degrees of organization that would be unimaginable elsewhere.

The evenness of the equatorial climate is described by Richards (1951). There are brighter, wetter and hotter places, but none so mild as the equatorial forest region. The diurnal and seasonal changes are slight, and cyclonic air movements unusual. This evenness of tempo stretches over geological time, for the last glaciations probably never brought a killing frost to the Equator.

The plants can grow very slowly, and in the course of this development be closely adapted to one another and to the land.

At first, when there has been a clearing or on new land, one or a few kinds of tree shoot up, occupying the ground fast but incompletely. Often they seem to exhaust themselves, and die off for no apparent reason. In disturbed places, trees rather like this, of few kinds, succeed each other. There are frequent gaps, which the commonest fast-growing tree occupies, becoming still commoner. Also the wind gets in, and favours thick and branchy trees against slender ones, the branches fighting.

This sort of wood can establish itself in twenty years, while equatorial forest may be developing after 600, as at Angkor (Richards 1951).

Here it is the plants which can establish themselves somewhere and last that preponderate. In this way, they explore the ground and one another. No wind gets in, and slender trees creep up next the great ones. They scarcely fight except as seedlings. The forest becomes a mosaic of hundreds of species, gradually higher, darker inside, and probably with some of the roots growing deeper. No nutrient or soil leaks out. This is all described by Richards, and the slow growth has been measured since. (Report 1953.)

This is what Rafael meant by clean forest. The association of buttressed trees with dirty forest would be due to both growing on flooded ground. The Cecropias are characteristic of new growth in this region.

All the same, there is no permanent distinction between the new forest and the old. The gaps left by fallen trees, in the soil conditions of the old forest, allow high and rapid new growth: this in turn preserves the tranquillity of the surrounding old. All the interior forest is a patchwork of relatively old and new bits; and its development may depend on each bit passing from new to old repeatedly. The better it is suited to the ground, the slower it will change.

NOTES (4)

Reflection of the forest in the Animals

ONE gets an impression that the plants of the interior forest dominate and exclude the animals. It struck me once that animals move around and plants don't, so that a quiet tempo favours the plants. This is not quite true, for the seeds move, and many of the animals remain still.

It is more true that the checks and opportunities of plant life are reflected the same way in the animals in any place. The plants with least opportunity present least, and so do the animals that eat them.

(*i*) *Deep Shade*
In the deepest shade, very heavy seeds germinate, and the seedlings, after using their food reserves, occasionally rise to a few metres in some hundred years. They are pencil-thin, with a few heavy leaves, lasting indefinitely. They gain the light eventually and fruit some years. It is probable that the fruiting is restricted by the food reserves; if so, the bigger the fewer, other things being equal.

Other plants here do not even gain the light, but mature very slowly in the shade. Some of these, tree-ferns and cycads, are among the slowest growing plants known.

These trees are heavy on the ground. They restrict one another severely, and if any individual is weakened, another gains by it. They have very little opportunity and cannot afford losses.

The wood is dark and hard. The seeds are woody, and may be even harder. The leaves are often stiff and harsh, with hard waxes or fibres. Also, automatically, a plant short of nourishment, unless temporarily dying off, nourishes whatever depends on it slowly.

I don't know what eats these plants. The living leaves are

untouched, and the debris rather empty. In these places there are animals such as the scorpion, the Ponerine ants, the flatworm possibly, and the tortoises.

Except for the flatworm, which is of a primitive order, these are all the slowest and most primitive animals of their kind. They all have special means of protection; and the more primitive animals of any group are usually to be handled with care. In each the tissues live in spite of damaging or stopping the central nervous system, at least for a time. They have a slow metabolism, growing and breeding slowly, except possibly the flatworm. They don't watch or search very acutely: even to keep a still watch requires quite rapid expenditure of energy. They are in places where there is little food, and all, except again the flatworm, have close relatives in the harshest deserts. In places with more opportunity they don't live; they are out-paced. They are tenacious of life.

In every respect they match the cycads, and in most the other trees of the shade.

(ii) The Interior Forest

The patches of uniform gloom are rare and accidental. In most of the forest there are bits of heavy and of moderate shade, with a fleck or two of sun visible from where one stands. Some of the seeds are heavy, giving a start in the shade, and some winged, gaining the lighter patches.

According to the opportunity, slow or faster growing trees arise, or vines, all scattered, and perhaps depending on the kinds neighbouring them. There is no kind of plant absent or in profusion, and seldom two of a species side by side.

Some of the individuals here have opportunity, but the local races have very little. At every point, it is hundreds to one against a particular species establishing itself, or regaining its place if weakened.

Every now and then one sees a butterfly, long-winged beetle (Buprestid or Longicorn), cicada, hunting wasp, or possibly a lower termite queen. These are comparable with the winged seeds, going far.

The larvae, and the permanently slow or stationary animals such as the leaf-insects, the cockroach already mentioned, tree frogs, vine-snake, geckos (one seen by

147

accident), most of the spiders and tree-creeping birds are not seen. They resemble the particular seeds, lichens, leaves or shoots that they live among, without any visible difference. The plant-eating ones are strictly confined to these one or two species. Except that they occur on few plants, even of these kinds, one might almost consider them as parts of the same.

In the Lepidoptera one can see fairly well how this comes about. All those of the interior forest are perfectly adapted to disperse their larvae. These are such as the butterflies described, Urania and thin hawk-moths. They have powerful wings for the size of abdomen and long tongues; they all take food occasionally on their way. Flying with great agility, and well coloured for rapid concealment, they cover the distance by day. The spiders would be one reason. Except for Pyralidae, probably feeding in the forest litter, there would be few moths or other insects at night.

They cannot carry much weight of eggs and keep their agility: they breed lightly. With few eggs per brood, it is necessary that the caterpillars should not compete with or betray each other, and they are on separate twigs and plants over the forest.

Consequently, if they compete at all it is between broods, not within them. The death of each caterpillar makes a relatively great genetic difference to the local race. This is in contrast to heavy broods all on one plant, in which the survivors are much the same genetically as the dead; and are favoured by the thinning out. Among the caterpillars of the lightly breeding species, there is intense selection against being eaten.

Where there are heavily and light-breeding Lepidoptera, the latter always attack different plants from the former. Presumably they avoid much hunting that way. But the heavily breeding kinds, which will be described later, are indiscriminate. They eat any plant they can. In Europe, there are mostly deciduous trees and shrubs, and most heavily-breeding species eat much the same. It follows, more or less, that the plants the lightly-breeding species attack are immune to others for some particular reason. Each species is particularly adapted to eat one or two such plants. This is true of all the agile and day-flying Lepidoptera, and of the other characteristic insects of the interior forest.

In some cases it is known what the difference is between the plants eaten by the heavily-breeding and by the lightly-breeding insects. The gipsy moth eats anything not containing various peculiar substances that poison or repel it (Kurir 1953). Various butterfly caterpillars will only eat leaves containing one or another particular substance, of exactly the kinds that discourage the gipsy moth (see Dethier, 1951). This is borne out by the number of known poisonous plants attacked by the fastest butterflies and Sphingidae (e.g. quoted by Moss 1920).

Whether because they are poisonous or not, the plants of the interior forest are not attacked by any indiscriminate insect. Sievers and others (1949) found that insects were poisoned by about 50 per cent of the species they tested from forest rather like this.

These plants are under the same conditions that they impose on the butterflies. They are dispersed, and the effective rate of breeding is light, because nearly all the seeds fail.

The same necessity, pretty much, is imposed on the animals that eat the larvae. These are to be hunted on particular plants, for one thing: some plants won't yield any at all. The selection against being eaten leads to such perfect resemblances, that it must be a specialized craft to find any one kind. In other cases, the larvae as of Buprestid beetles or lower termites are concealed in dense wood. Each kind must be sought out in its own place. The same rules of dispersion and light breeding apply to the hunters of each, and perhaps to those that hunt them, and so on.

Accordingly there is a great number of species only attacking one or two sorts of food. These are nearly all the species in the forest: those which eat a variety of things are of relatively few species.

(iii) Disturbed Patches
Quick-growing trees, comparable and often related to the weeds of wasteland, grow in dense masses in these places. The patch of a particular species is often not of great extent,

but is confined by those neighbouring it. It may be partly an accident which species gets away in any particular place. The conditions for fast growth don't last, and the invading plants die out as the forest develops. They are carried from one patch to the next on very light fluffy seeds, or else by animals in fruit or burrs.

There are sporadic conditions for heavy breeding, but with the necessity for dispersal.

In these places one finds many brightly marked and repellent animals. In this forest there were Mutillid wasps, Coccinellid and Chrysomelid beetles, a large weevil (black with zigzag red stripes), certain Pentatomid and many Pyrocorrhid bugs, probably some relatively heavy-breeding Danaidae, and also Crax and the black and yellow birds. They were harshly coloured, relatively slow, fat and unwary. The fast flash-coloured ones, which vanish when seen, are entirely different. Very few of the repellent animals were in the interior forest.

Similar aposematic animals live in wasteland elsewhere: such are the Arctiidae, Castniidae and Zygaenidae among moths, the Colorado beetle, Magpie, Goldfinch and Skunk. It is because of experiments on these, that one can be sure similar animals repel their enemies. The markings don't prove it, but the way they act. They all go slowly and obviously by day. They carry many eggs or young, and occur in groups among the clumps of vegetation where they feed.

They have the same capacity for heavy breeding, combined with the same necessity of dispersal, as the plants on which they depend. If anything eats them, they present it with the same necessity in turn. It is bound to look for some particular species of prey, because nothing can eat different ones: it must hunt this prey in appropriate places; but if lucky it can eat much at a time. This is probably why most of these aposematic animals are confined to plants which occur in masses. On a thinly dispersed food-plant they would be too vulnerable.

A peculiar resemblance is that the plants as well as the animals are largely poisonous or repulsive. Such are ragworts, spurges, thistles, nettles and nightshade in wastelands; various Solanaceae, Euphorbiaceae, Anacardiaceae, Apocynaceae and tropical nettles in new patches of rain-forest. None of them is eaten indiscriminately. I think these plants are well known because they tend to discourage mammals in particular. The nettles contain mammalian hormones. Mammal browsing might be too heavy for plants like this, which grow in limited patches.

It also seems characteristic of small patches, that few large and indiscriminate hunting populations go through them. The absence of *Tambochas* and the scarity of *Eciton* in the interior forest of the Macarena is mentioned. The aposematic insects, both in the Macarena and in wasteland clumps, appear to show this. Where there are predators feeding heavily and indiscriminately, the poisonous insects show Müllerian mimicry. In these small patches they show quite the opposite. The patterns are so bizarre and elaborate that there cannot be even a coincidental resemblance. Each is protected from the particular predators which attack the others.

(iv) Areas and Times of Opportunity

In the forest, the areas of opportunity are the fringes, river banks, flooded areas and old farmland. I don't know them well. Rather the same plants grow as in the little disturbed patches; but also aggressive grasses and giant herbs. Many of them are dispersed by animals.

The times of opportunity, not only in these places but everywhere, are those of more or less rampant growth, fruiting, and the dying-off of evanescent plants. The plants can afford attack at such times, and are commonly most nourishing then.

These places and times are exploited by big and fast-moving societies such as leaf-cutting ants, army ants, peccaries, parrots and macaws, squirrel and spider monkeys. Bates (1892) mentions the smaller birds of the upper Amazon forest, of many species, hunting in a big crowd. These societies are possibly analogous with the great herds of nomadic ungulates, which cross grasslands according to the seasonal changes and the fires. The leaf-cutting ants are settled, but range far. The maximum distance quoted is a mile (Weber).

The opportunity, both for plants and for animals, is evanescent. In the forest, the areas are unstable. In grassland, there is drought. The animals can't feed in any of these places permanently. Eventually they have to go, and the larger the scale of disturbance, the further.

It seems that the further the animals go, the bigger are their societies. Those in the grasslands are biggest, and go furthest. One can see roughly how this happens from animals that form temporary societies, such as Voles, Lemmings, Robins and Locusts. In rich conditions they are settled and live separately, mostly holding individual territories. When food supplies dwindle, the territory, which is limited by their speed and capacity to frighten one another, won't any longer support an individual or family. They must move, and this is when they join up. They cannot go as territory-holding individuals without interfering with one another; and it may be less dangerous to migrate together. Those going furthest would interfere with one another even in moderate-sized groups, and form enormous groups that can hardly ever meet. Such are the super-colonies of ants.

From the silence, and the absence even of a dawn chorus in the rain-forest, it seems there is hardly any opportunity for settled individual life. Nearly all the fast animals go far across it, in bands that only appear at long intervals in any place.

The groups that hold joint territories in the rain-forest, such as the howler-monkeys and possibly the macaws, are relatively small, and live off enormous areas, about as their voices carry.

NOTES (5)

Conclusion

Recurrent and Continuous Opportunity

IT's an obvious rule of natural activities that they're discontinuous. Different things control the period in each case, and it would be a mathematician's job to interpret this as a general law. It also seems that where the activity of plants is most periodic, it is fastest and least elaborate. Where the plants work fastest, there are the most animals, and of the fewest kinds.

The growth of tissue in a young leaf rises and falls. At some time, its ultimate extent is determined. I shall assume that development is not completed till after this has happened. If it happens so that the final size is reached at the peak of total growth, then the area grows at the quickest possible rate in that single leaf. Further delay involves slack time, when growth has declined, though the ultimate size is greater.

Over a long time the slow growth of big leaves may overlap, adding up to a fast total production. There are two limitations to this. Big leaves are usually formed at longer intervals than short small ones, and are ill-spaced otherwise. Also, there is slack time at the beginning and end of the succession.

This is really a problem in wave analysis, which the plants solve as follows. A given period of growth is broken into phases of a length directly related to the total period. These overlap more the longer (and slower) they are.

Unbranched stems growing for a long period have big leaves, slowly formed, and overlapping in age by months or years.

Leaves may be built up in the same way. This permits big leaves to develop each at as fast an average rate as a quick succession of small ones. The difference is that, except in ferns, the leaf eventually expands as a whole, and new development ceases. The phases within leaf formation are in the protection of the bud, especially in thick, buried or heavily-shaded ones.

The margin of a newly-formed leaf beginning to develop in concealment commonly bulges, and often breaks into blobs, from the tip downwards. This may happen repeatedly. I think the manner of growth depends on how early it happens in each case; how soon the veins form, or perhaps thicken; and when the leaf comes to light (or turns green):

(a) The earlier the margin bulges, the less elongated the whole leaf.

(b) Usually, the quicker the succession of blobs or bulges, the less time they each grow out.

(c) They grow out separately in the dark, but tend to fuse if still growing after emergence.

(d) Their growth halts as the veins form. The veins and margin are therefore fixed, but extend a determined amount on emergence if this is later.

(e) The earlier in development veins form, the more tissue grows between them. It becomes folded, especially before emergence.

(f) Likewise, the earlier in development the leaf emerges, the more tissue formed afterwards.

(g) Before the veins form, the tissue is smooth, soft and simple. Afterwards, before emergence, it grows thinner and often hairy, still soft. After emergence it thickens, hardens and diversifies. Parts form oil, resin, latex, wax or other substances, and the surface is coated.

(h) This is a gradual course of development; but in some tropical plants the final leaf type is apparent from the start.

(i) Grass blades grow in rather the same way as a single bulge in a net-veined leaf.

*　　　*　　　*　　　*

Rapid growth over a short period is reflected in a divided,

154

serrated or bulgy margin and pronounced development of the veins. The longer the succession of marginal outgrowths (and the bigger the leaf), the less tissue formed after emergence. Sometimes the leaves are smoothish and finely divided, in herbs and soft grasses; sometimes hairy, broad, folded and floppy, also in herbs; long, corrugated, tough and shiny but light, with serrated margin in deciduous trees; small, hard, with a few shallow spiny points in shrubs.

Such details reflect the character of the plant. The succession of phases of growth is rather similar in leaf-margins, shoot and branch. Short-phase leaves are also formed in very rapid succession, or almost simultaneously, on all the shoots in the plant. Then they are active for a limited period, and die. This is complete in herbs and deciduous trees, partial in hard-leaved shrubs, which go bare from the top down after a summer drought. Reproduction is more complicated, but I think it is likewise rapid and over a short period. The flowers are either showy or wind-pollinated. At the end of the growing season, if it lives longer, the plant stores food.

Plants of this kind take up from the soil and return to it every year large amounts of the materials of life, in relation to the shade they cast. This is indicated by the anatomy of the leaves, except in hard-leaved shrubs, which receive much radiation. These plants demand good soil, light and adequate water, all three in the growing season. Conversely, the more demanding plants in rain-forests, where no particular growing season is imposed by the climate, have one. It is different in different species (Richards 1951 pp. 193 ff; Capon 1947). It shows in their timber. Ladefoged (1952) indicates that the growing season of shoots is consistently longer and less definite in the less demanding of various temperate trees. At the end of their life, short phase leaves fall with a large amount of nutrients still in them. An example is given by Viro (1956); generally such leaves yield rich humus. The amounts of nutrients in the leaves, twigs, fruit and bark falling every year, and sometimes those in the rain-drip from the foliage (Tamm 1951), have been measured in a few temperate and tropical forests and grass lands (References B: there's too little of this evidence, and it's mostly in Russian). The yearly turn-over of Calcium and Potassium, in relation to the shade cast, is consistently highest in deciduous forest and in soft grassland. In a given climate and soil, it is absolutely highest from such vegetation.

Also, the amounts of nutrients becoming available in the soil every year are greatest where its activity is most strongly periodic. This is in continental climates compared with oceanic ones, and in middle latitudes compared with the highest and lowest. These places are where short-phase plants preponderate. Their seasons are timed by the weather, but their manner of growth not imposed by it.

Depending on climate and soil, there seems to be a limit to the possible turn-over of nutrients, at least through a given type of vegetation; possibly through any type. In oak forests from 25 to 225 years there was hardly any change (Mina 1955). The growth of the foliage each year is self-limiting, and more so, the more active the leaves. If short-phase plants are lopped, grazed or defoliated, they regenerate briskly, and the normal turn-over is re-established.

Animals feeding on them are thus a load on the turn-over. They pass a fraction of it through themselves, without necessarily reducing it. If the fraction is too great, they will reduce it, due to loss of nutrients in the rain-wash, reduced activity of the plants, and growth of less active plants. The land goes sour. This happens least readily where the activity of each leaf is greatest; and these places carry the heaviest animal populations, including man.

In these animals and plants, different populations of a species live in quite different ways. Either individuals or local races vary, partly fitting themselves to the conditions. Their modes of life are rather simple, and the species few, especially those with a long life. Precisely defined behaviour as in the rain-forest is unusual; except in short life-cycles, as of insects and low herbs, the seasonal changes preclude such refinements.

The species are not closely controlled in density, and tend to dominate particular areas, excluding competitors. Often their dominance in one place and absence from another cannot be convincingly ascribed to the conditions.

In animals such as rodents and lagomorphs, heavy moths, beetles and snails, local clumps are formed by heavy breeding. For example, among moths, the Lymantriidae, Psychidae, Cheimatobiinae (fat geometers), many Saturniidae and Smerinthinae (fat Sphingidae, an artificial group) all feed in patches on deciduous trees or on shrubs, most on many kinds. They have short or rudimentary tongues, and the females are clumsy in the air or even wingless. If they fly, it's at night. The males have comb-like antennae, scenting and gathering to the females from afar. The females drop large masses of eggs, often on no particular food-plant. Nearly all the larvae are killed off most years; only the older ones and the pupae are scattered and protected.

Other species, especially those storing food or remaining active over the winter, are too irritable or predatory to live with. This needs no illustration.

*   *   *   *

Leaves grown at a slow rate are smooth-edged, and moderately or weakly veined. Typical examples are broad, soft and smooth in shade-tolerant vines; long and leathery in evergreen trees; stiff, narrow and greyish, sometimes vertical in conifers and tall-growing evergreen scrub; likewise in sedges compared with soft grasses.

The manner of growth and reproduction in such plants, the conditions tolerated, timing of activity, nutrient content of leaves, and control of growth are all in contrast to those qualities in short-phase plants.

The essential difference is that the activity of the leaves is lower, and the limits of growth higher, and gradually attained. The turn-over of nutrients is thus much less readily maintained or restored. At least in evergreen conifers, there's little tolerance of heavy damage.

This is a sign of specialization of different parts for different roles, which can be seen partially. In the rainforest shade it goes very far. The reproductive shoots are early separate from the leafy ones, different regions of the stem develop differently, and the parts of each kind are reduced in number (see Richards 1951 Ch. 4). These plants have an animal look.

The amount of animal life in bogs, sedge moors and healthy conifer forests seems to be low. Allee (1926) and Sanderson (1944) found the same thing in rain-forest. Other observers think the animals are quite abundant, but too subtle to be seen; they have no evidence, and anyway the leaves aren't eaten. What is certain is that these animals breed lightly and are hard to kill. There's a rather high proportion of nitrogen to mineral nutrients in the leaves, and this might result directly in the growth of sterile animal matter, as in the workers of social insects and in the decoration, defence or camouflage of solitary ones. I'm indebted to Dr Borrero for suggesting that some of the feathers I had admired in his birds could have passed beyond natural selection.

REFERENCES

Allee, W. C., 1926 (Rain-forest animals) Ecology 7, pp. 445 ff.

Bates, H. W., 1892, The Naturalist on the River Amazons, London.

Bates, M., 1948 (Rain-forest, rainfall, fire) Geog. Rev. 38.

Capon, M., 1947 (Rain-forest growing seasons) C. R. de la Semaine Agricole de Yangambi, INEAC 849-62.

Carpenter, C. R., 1934 (Howler monkeys) Comp. Psychol. Monog. 10, pp. 1-168.

Dethier, V. G., 1951 (Caterpillar feeding preferences) 9th Int. Cong. Ent. Symposium IV (2), pp. 97 ff (Amsterdam 1953).

Jenny, H., 1949 (Colombian soil groups) Soil Sci. 66, pp. 5-28.

Kurir, A., 1953 (Gipsy moth caterpillar) Z. Angew Ent. 34 (4), pp. 543-86.

Ladefoged, K., 1952 (Periodic growth) Dan. Biol. Skr. 7 (3).

Moss, M., 1920 (Sphingid caterpillars) Nov. Zool. 27.

Pitt, C. J. W., Unpubl. (Fire in rain-forest) FAO: ETAP (a forthcoming report).

Report, 1953, Slow Growth in Virgin Forest Confirmed, Caribb. For. 14, p. 7.

Richards, P. W., 1951, The Tropical Rain Forest, Cambridge.

Sanderson, I., 1944, Living Treasure, Viking, N.Y.

Schmidt, D., 1948 (Colombian rainfall) Bonn Geog. Abhandlungen 9, p. 106.

Sievers, A. F. et al, 1949 (Tropical plant insecticides) J. Econ. Ent. 42 p. 549.

Weber, N. A. (Leaf-cutting ants) Rev. Ent. Rio de Janeiro, 1937-46, 8 p. 265, 9 p. 154, 12 p. 93, 16 p. 1, 17 p. 114.

Wheeler, W. M., 1942 (Azteca and plants) Bull. Harvard Mus. Comp. Zool. 90.

B: TURN-OVER OF NUTRIENTS

Metz, L. J., 1952 (S.E., U.S.A.) Res. Note Stheast. For. Expt. Sta. 14.

Mina, V. N., 1955 (Russia) Počvoved 6 32-44, summary in For. Abst. 17 (2) No 1145.

Jenny, H., 1949 (Colombia) Soil Sci. 66 (3) p. 173.

Laudelout, H., Meyer, J., 1954 (Congo) Trans. 5th Int. Cong. Soil Sci., 2, pp. 267-72.

Nye, P. H., 1961 (Ghana) Plant and Soil, 13 (4), pp. 333-46.

Remezov, N. P., (Russia) Trans. 6th Int. Cong. Soil Sci., Vol E, pp. 269-74.

Scott, D. R. M., 1955 (E. U.S.A.) Bull. Yale Sch. For. 62.

Tamm, C. O., 1951 (Rain drip) Physiol. Plant., Copenhagen 4 (1) 184-8.

Viro, P. J., 1956 (Finland) Commun. Inst. For. Fenn. 45 (6).